MW00388635

Favourite Piano Classics I

for piano · für Klavier · pour piano

Compiled and provided with fingering by
Zusammengestellt und mit Fingersatz versehen von
Rédigé et doigté par

Ágnes Lakos

Könemann Music Budapest
K 128

CONTENTS

Page

Jean François Dandrieu (1682–1738)
Les fifres (The Whistlers) 8
La gémissante (The Heaver of Sighs) 11

Jean Philippe Rameau (1683–1764)
Tambourin 13

François Couperin (1668–1733)
Le coucou (The Cuckoo) 15

Louis-Claude Daquin (1694–1772)
Le coucou (The Cuckoo) 16

Johann Sebastian Bach (1685–1750)
Praeludium, F Major, BWV 927 21
Praeludium, D Minor, BWV 926 22
Praeludium, C Minor (Lute Prelude), BWV 999 24
Praeludium, E Minor, BWV 938 26
Praeludium, D Minor, BWV 935 28
Praeludium, D Major, BWV 936 30
Menuet (from the French Suite in B Minor), BWV 813/V 32
Gavotte (from the French Suite in G Major), BWV 816/IV 34
Sarabande (from the French Suite in D Minor), BWV 812/III 35
Praeludium, C Major (from "The Well-Tempered Clavichord I"), BWV 846 36

Georg Friedrich Händel (1685–1759)
Sarabande (from the Suite in D Minor), HWV 437/IV 38
Air (from the Suite in E Major) "The Harmonius Blacksmith", HWV 430/IV 40
Chaconne, G Major, HWV 435 44

Domenico Scarlatti (1685–1757)
Sonata, D Minor, K1, L 366 . . . 52
Sonata, D Minor, K 9, L 413 . . . 54
Sonata, E Minor, K 98, L 325 . . . 56
Sonata, D Major, K 96, L 465 . . . 60
Sonata, A Major, K 113, L 345 . . . 64

Carl Philipp Emanuel Bach (1714-1788)
Solfeggio . . . 68
Variations upon "Ich schlief, da träumte mir" . . . 70

Joseph Haydn (1732–1809)
Ochsen-Menuett (Ox-Minuet) . . . 76
La Roxolane (Air varié) . . . 78

Wolfgang Amadeus Mozart (1756–1791)
Rondo alla turca ("Turkish March"), KV 331 (300^{i})/III . . . 82
Fantasie, D Minor, KV 397 (385^{g}) . . . 86
Rondo, D Major, KV 485 . . . 92

Ludwig van Beethoven (1770–1827)
6 Ecossaissen, WoO 83 . . . 100
Für Elise, WoO 59 . . . 104
Bagatell, C Major, Op. 33, No. 2. . . . 108
Bagatell, F Major, Op. 33, No. 3. . . . 112
Bagatell, G Minor, Op. 119, No. 1. . . . 114
Bagatell, A Minor, Op. 119, No. 9. . . . 116
Rondo, C Major, Op. 51, No. 1. . . . 117

Carl Maria von Weber (1786–1826)
Momento capriccioso, Op. 12. . . . 126
Aufforderung zum Tanz (Invitation to the Dance), Op. 65. . . . 133

Franz Schubert (1797–1828)
Scherzo, B♭ Major, D 593 . . . 143
Allegretto, C Minor, D 915 . . . 146
Moment musical, F minor, "Air russe", Op. 94, No. 3, D 780 . . . 150
Impromptu, A♭ Major, Op. post. 142, D 935 . . . 152

INHALT

Jean François Dandrieu (1682–1738) Seite
Les fifres (Die Pfeifer) 8
La gémissante (Die Seufzerin) 11

Jean Philippe Rameau (1683–1764)
Tambourin 13

François Couperin (1668–1733)
Le coucou (Der Kuckuck) 15

Louis-Claude Daquin (1694–1772)
Le coucou (Der Kuckuck) 16

Johann Sebastian Bach (1685–1750)
Praeludium, F-Dur BWV 927 21
Praeludium, d-Moll, BWV 926 22
Praeludium, c-Moll (Lautenpraeludium), BWV 999 24
Praeludium, e-Moll, BWV 938 26
Praeludium, d-Moll, BWV 935 28
Praeludium, D-Dur, BWV 936 30
Menuet (aus der Französischen Suite in h-Moll), BWV 813/V 32
Gavotte (aus der Französischen Suite in G-Dur), BWV 816/IV 34
Sarabande (aus der Französischen Suite in d-Moll), BWV 812/III 35
Praeludium, C-Dur (aus dem Wohltemperierten Klavier I), BWV 846 36

Georg Friedrich Händel (1685–1759)
Sarabande (aus der Suite in d-Moll), HWV 437/IV 38
Air (aus der Suite in E-Dur) "Der lustiger Schmied", HWV 430/IV 40
Chaconne, G-Dur, HWV 435 44

Domenico Scarlatti (1685–1757)
Sonata, d-Moll, K1, L 366 52
Sonata, d-Moll, K 9, L 413 54
Sonata, e-Moll, K 98, L 325 56
Sonata, D-Dur, K 96, L 465 60
Sonata, A-Dur, K 113, L 345 64

Carl Philipp Emanuel Bach (1714-1788)
Solfeggio 68
Variationen über "Ich schlief, da träumte mir" 70

Joseph Haydn (1732–1809)
Ochsen-Menuett 76
La Roxolane (Air varié) 78

Wolfgang Amadeus Mozart (1756–1791)
Rondo alla turca ("Türkischer Marsch"), KV 331 (300^{i})/III 82
Fantasie, d-Moll, KV 397 (385^{g}) 86
Rondo, D-Dur, KV 485 92

Ludwig van Beethoven (1770–1827)
6 Ecossaissen, WoO 83 100
Für Elise, WoO 59 104
Bagatell, C-Dur, Op. 33, No. 2. 108
Bagatell, F-Dur, Op. 33, No. 3. 112
Bagatell, g-Moll, Op. 119, No. 1. 114
Bagatell, a-Moll, Op. 119, No. 9. 116
Rondo, C-Dur, Op. 51, No. 1. 117

Carl Maria von Weber (1786–1826)
Momento capriccioso, Op. 12. 126
Aufforderung zum Tanz, Op. 65. 133

Franz Schubert (1797–1828)
Scherzo, B-Dur, D 593 143
Allegretto, c-Moll, D 915 146
Moment musical, f Moll, "Air russe", Op. 94, No. 3, D 780 150
Impromptu, As-Dur, Op. post. 142, D 935 152

CONTENU

Jean François Dandrieu (1682–1738) Page

Les fifres 8

La gémissante 11

Jean Philippe Rameau (1683–1764)

Tambourin 13

François Couperin (1668–1733)

Le coucou 15

Louis-Claude Daquin (1694–1772)

Le coucou 16

Johann Sebastian Bach (1685–1750)

Praeludium, fa majeur, BWV 927 21

Praeludium, re mineur, BWV 926 22

Praeludium, ut mineur (luth prélude), BWV 999 24

Praeludium, mi mineur, BWV 938 26

Praeludium, re mineur, BWV 935 28

Praeludium, re majeur, BWV 936 30

Menuet (de la Suite Françoise en si mineur), BWV 813/V 32

Gavotte (de la Suite Françoise en sol majeur), BWV 816/IV 34

Sarabande (de la Suite Françoise en re mineur), BWV 812/III 35

Praeludium, ut majeur (de "Le clavecin bien temperé I"), BWV 846 36

Georg Friedrich Händel (1685–1759)

Sarabande (de la Suite en re mineur), HWV 437/IV 38

Air (de la Suite en mi majeur) "Le forgeron gai", HWV 430/IV 40

Chaconne, sol majeur, HWV 435 44

Domenico Scarlatti (1685–1757)
Sonata, re mineur, K1, L 366 . . . 52
Sonata, re mineur, K 9, L 413 . . . 54
Sonata, mi mineur, K 98, L 325 . . . 56
Sonata, re majeur, K 96, L 465 . . . 60
Sonata, la majeur, K 113, L 345 . . . 64

Carl Philipp Emanuel Bach (1714-1788)
Solfeggio . . . 68
Variations sur "Ich schlief, da träumte mir" . . . 70

Joseph Haydn (1732–1809)
Ochsen-Menuett (Menuet de boeufs) . . . 76
La Roxolane (Air varié) . . . 78

Wolfgang Amadeus Mozart (1756–1791)
Rondo alla turca ("Marche turque"), KV 331 (300^{i})/III . . . 82
Fantasie, re mineur, KV 397 (385^{g}) . . . 86
Rondo, re majeur, KV 485 . . . 92

Ludwig van Beethoven (1770–1827)
6 Ecossaissen, WoO 83 . . . 100
Für Elise, WoO 59 . . . 104
Bagatell, ut majeur, Op. 33, No. 2 . . . 108
Bagatell, fa majeur, Op. 33, No. 3 . . . 112
Bagatell, sol mineur, Op. 119, No. 1 . . . 114
Bagatell, la mineur, Op. 119, No. 9 . . . 116
Rondo, ut majeur, Op. 51, No. 1 . . . 117

Carl Maria von Weber (1786–1826)
Momento capriccioso, Op. 12 . . . 126
Aufforderung zum Tanz, (L'invitation à la valse), Op. 65 . . . 133

Franz Schubert (1797–1828)
Scherzo, si♭ majeur, D 593 . . . 143
Allegretto, ut mineur, D 915 . . . 146
Moment musical, fa mineur, "Air russe", Op. 94, No. 3, D 780 . . . 150
Impromptu, la♭ majeur, Op. post. 142, D 935 . . . 152

Les fifres
Rondeau

1er Couplet

2e Couplet
Rondeau

La Gémissante
Rondeau

Affectueusement **(Con sentimento)**

J. F. Dandrieu

Rondeau

Tambourin

J. Ph. Rameau

25
30
35
40
46

Le coucou

F. Couperin

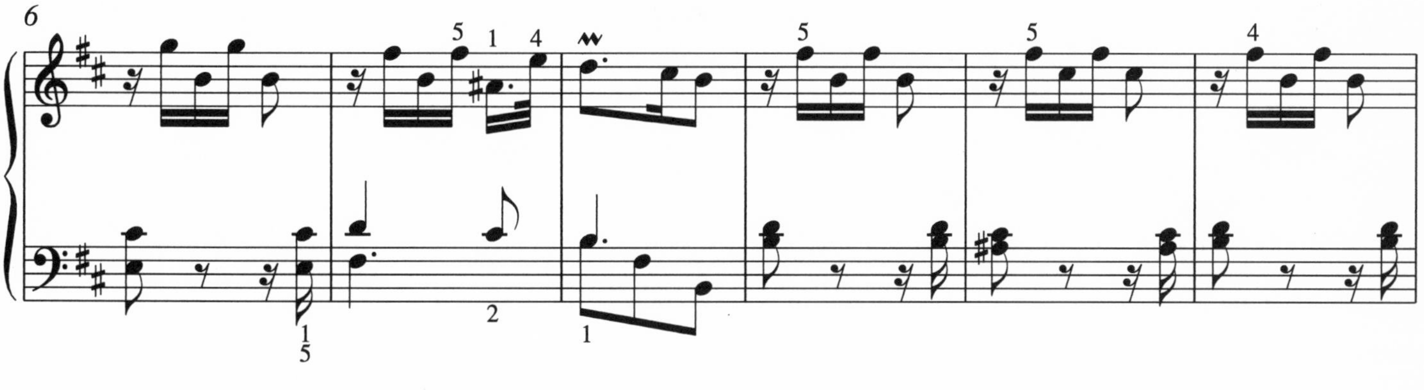

Le coucou
Rondeau

L. C. Daquin

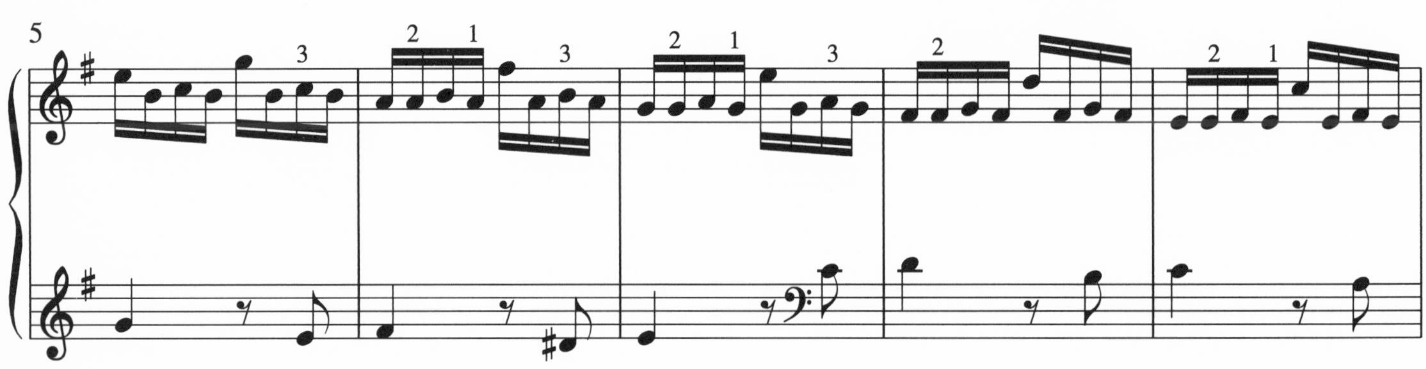

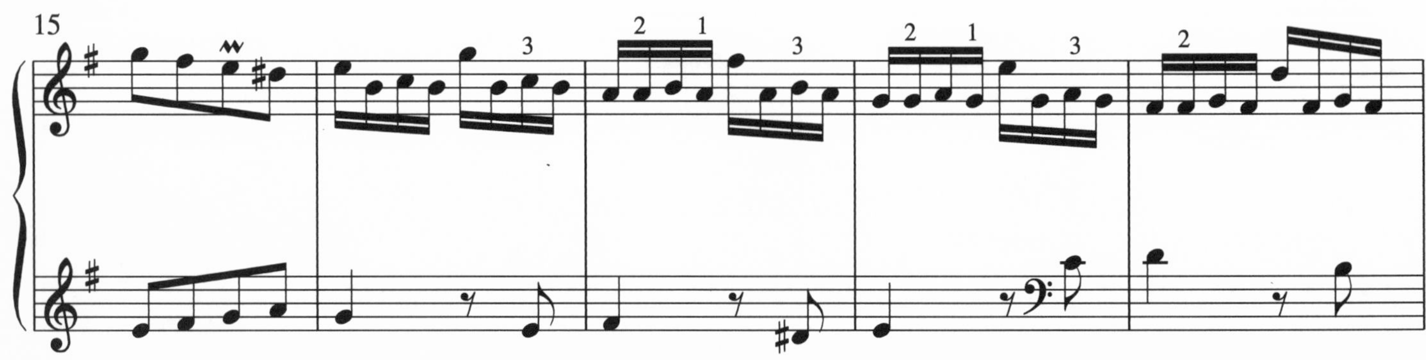

1er Couplet

Rondeau
2ème Couplet

68

73

78
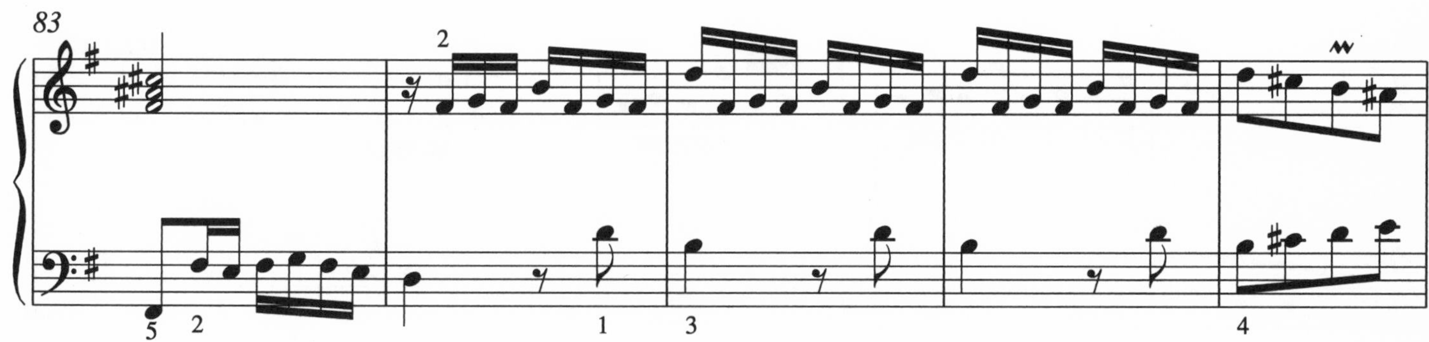
83
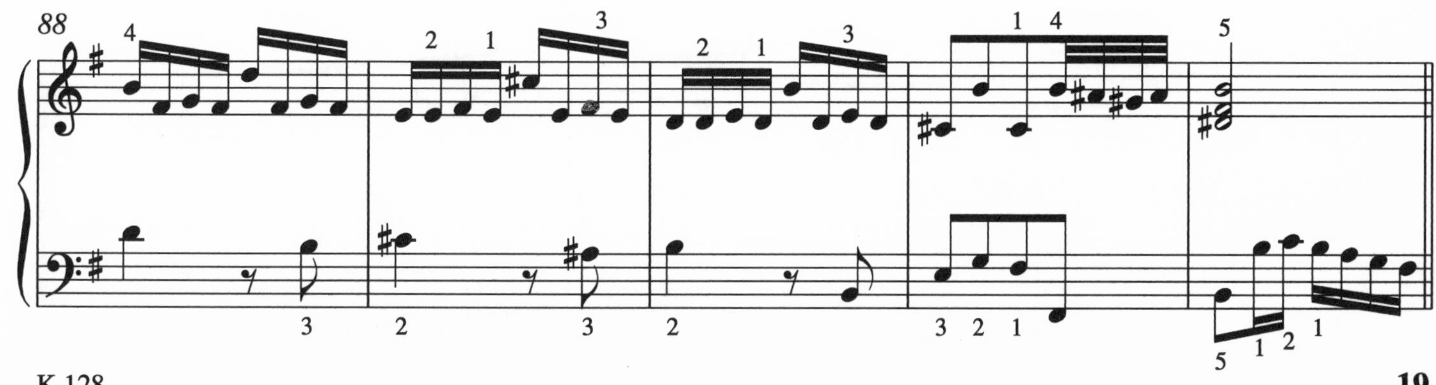
88

Rondeau

 K 128

Praeludium

BWV 927

J. S. Bach

Praeludium

BWV 926

J. S. Bach

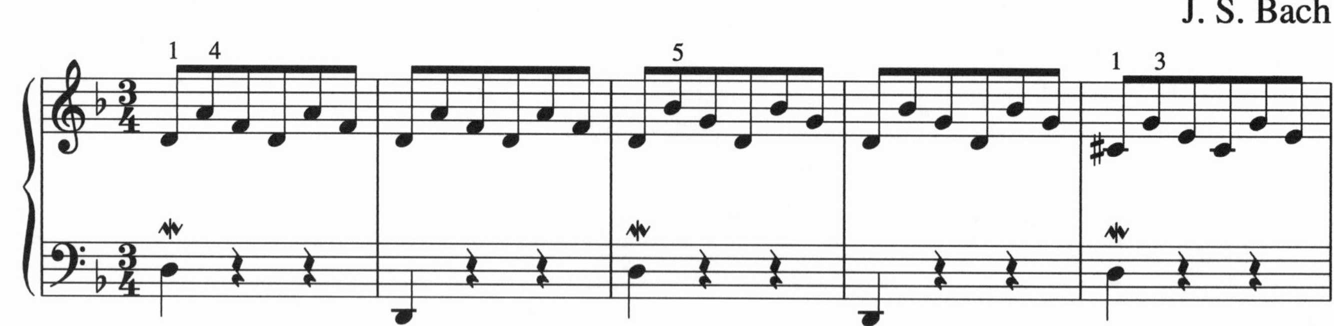

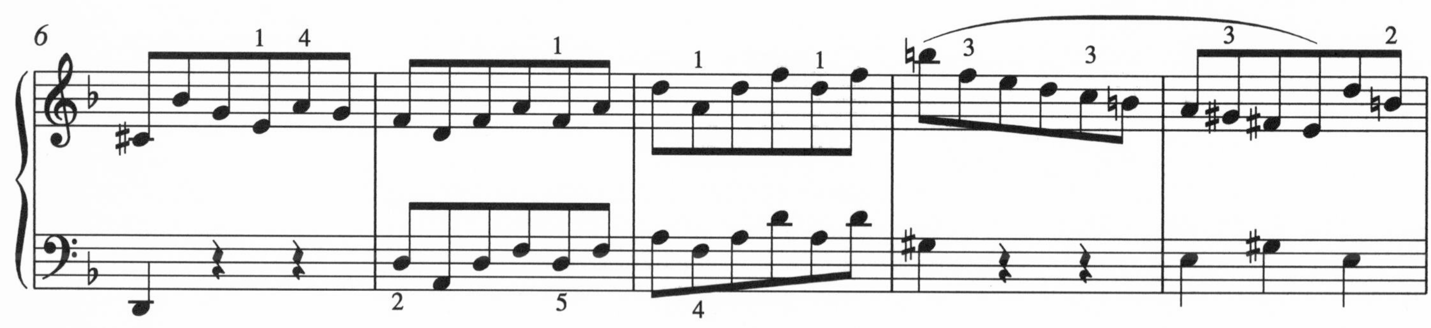

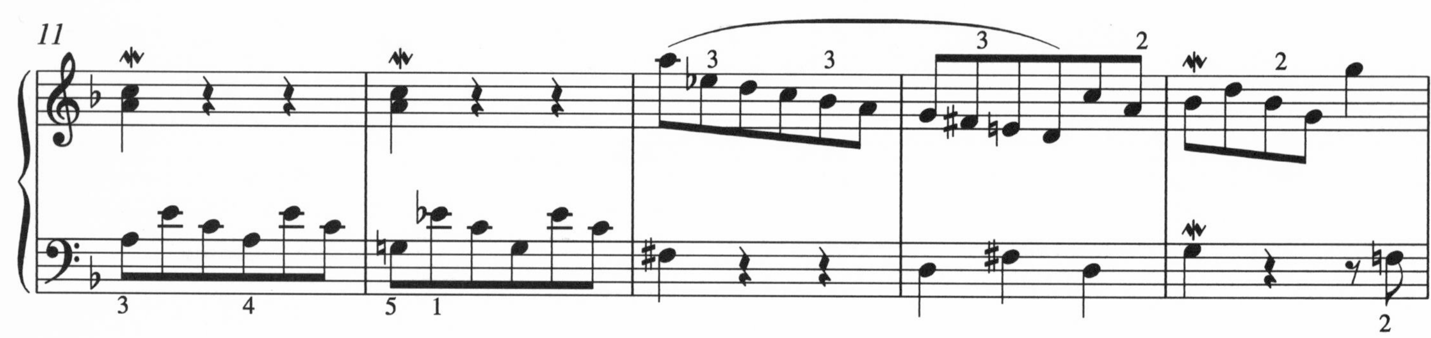

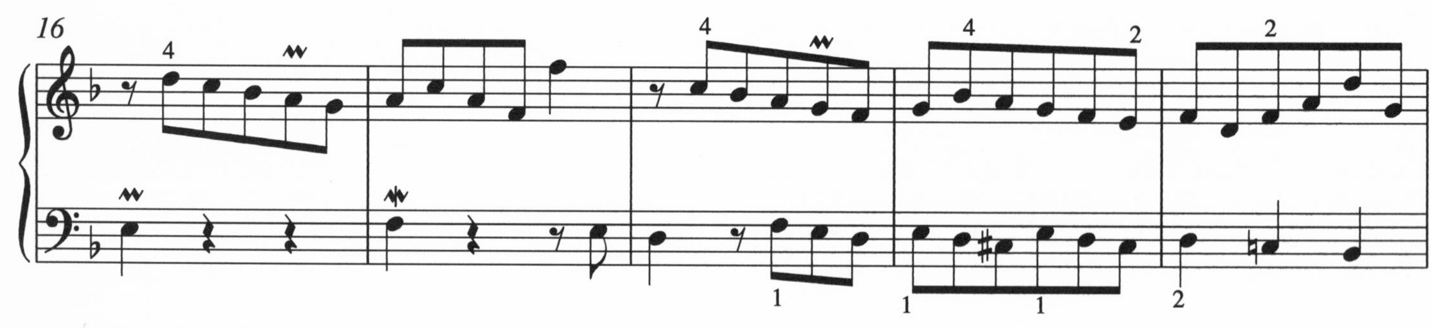

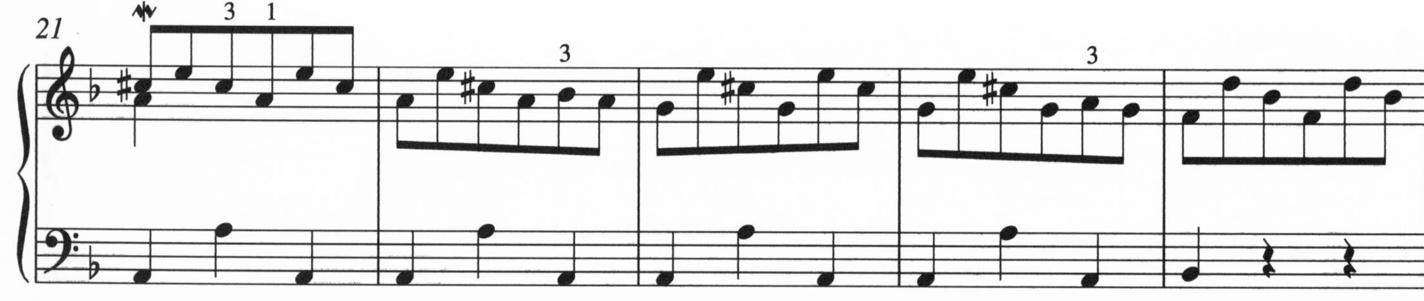

Praeludium

BWV 999

J. S. Bach

4

7

10

13

16

19

Praeludium

BWV 938

J. S. Bach

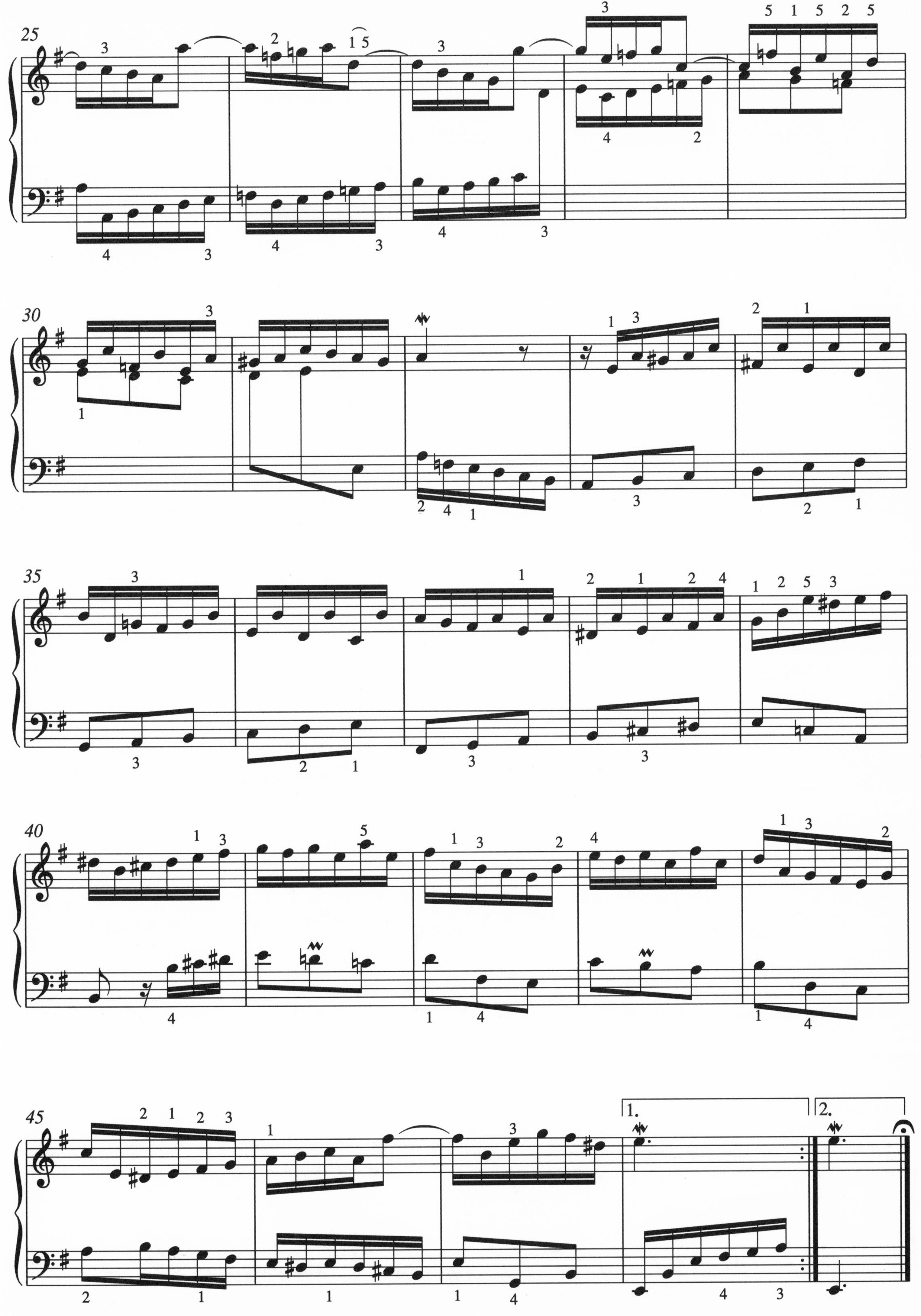

Praeludium

BWV 935

J. S. Bach

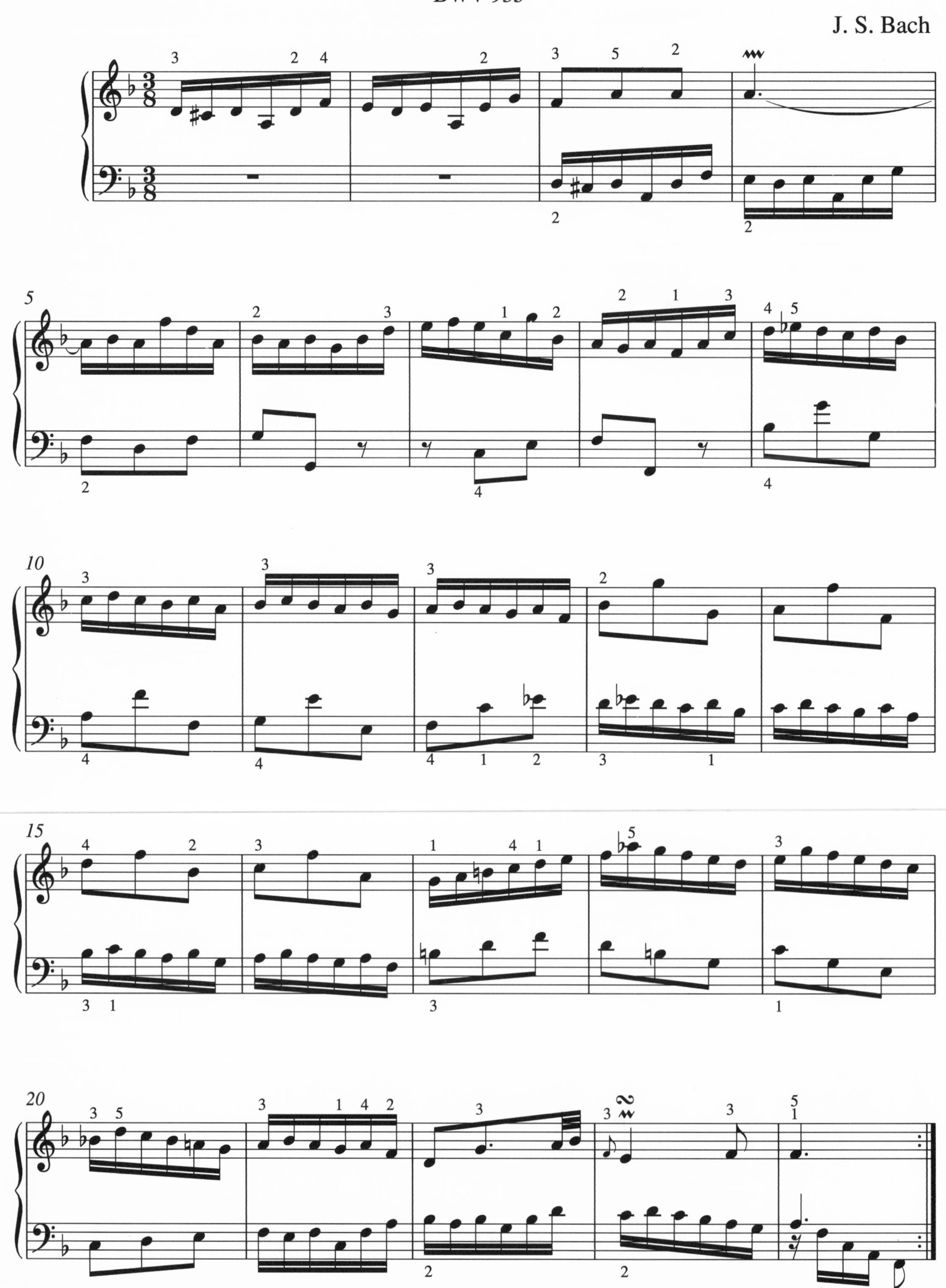

Praeludium

BWV 936

Menuet

BWV 813 / V

J. S. Bach

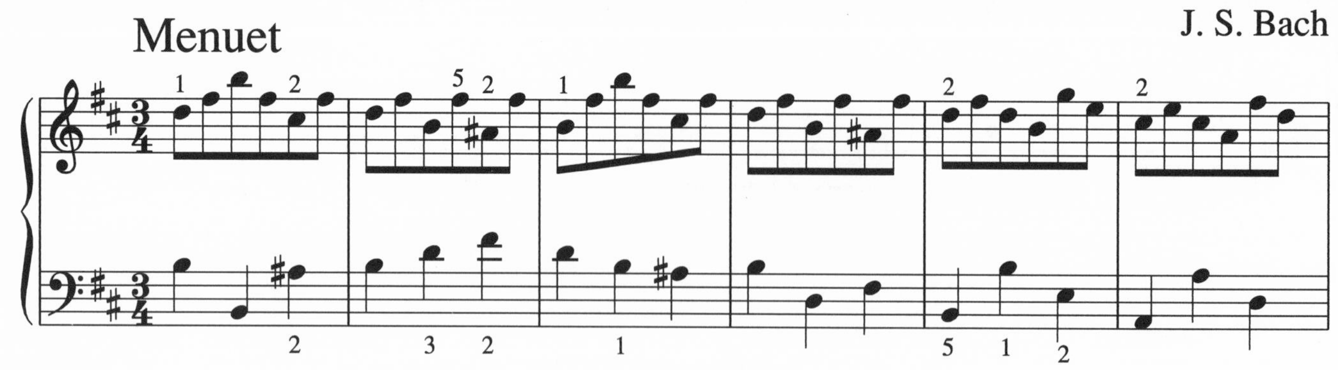

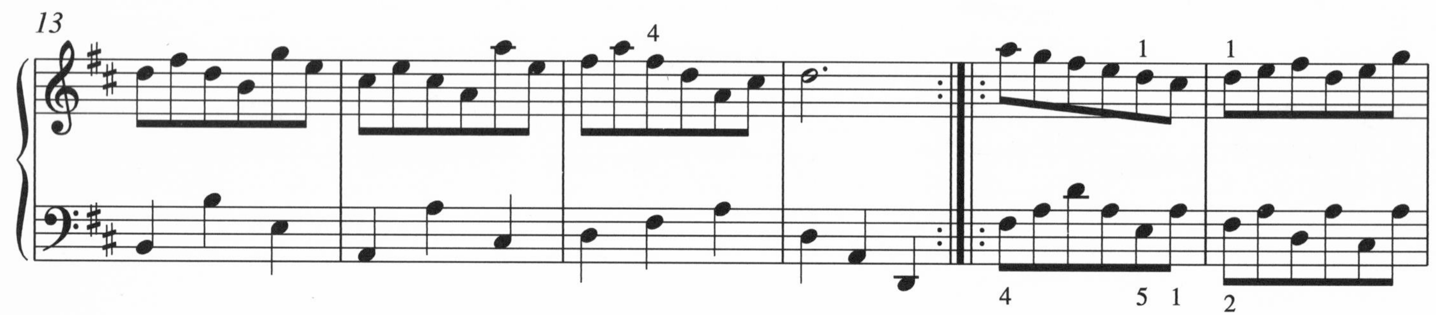

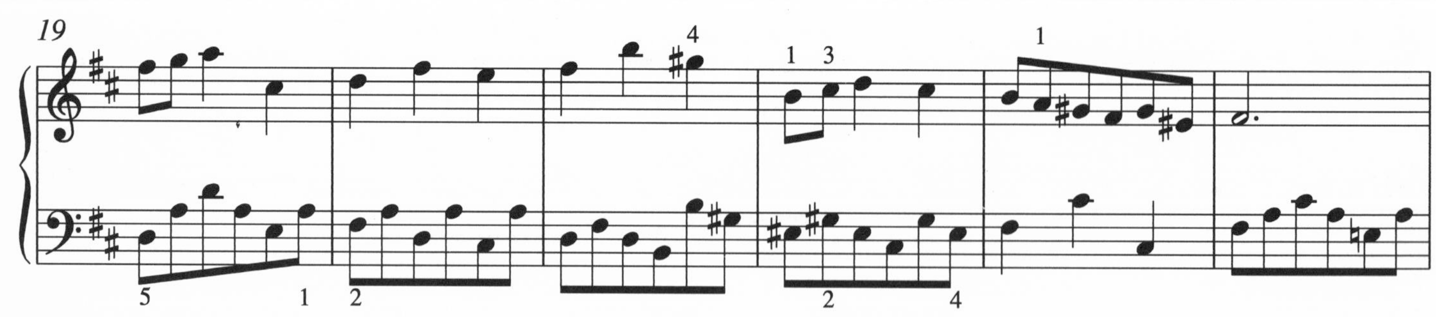

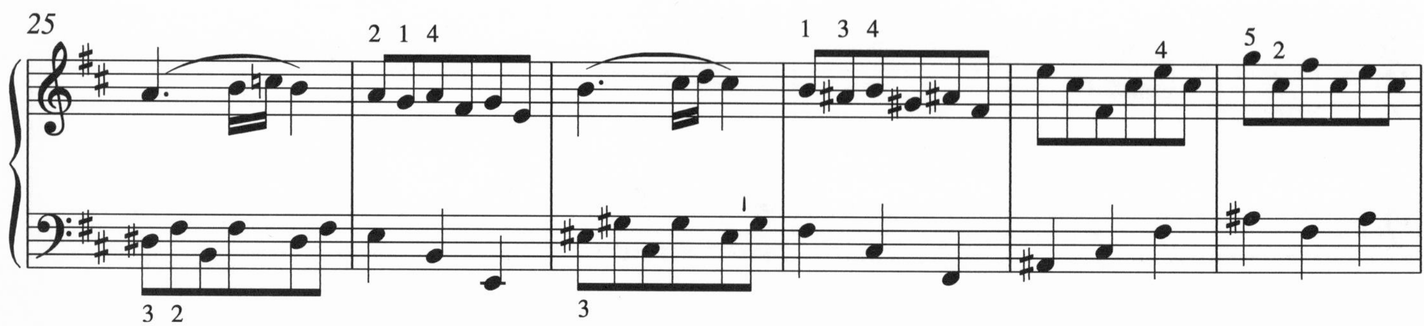

Trio
Menuet da Capo

Gavotte

BWV 816 / IV

J. S. Bach

Sarabande

BWV 812 / III

J. S. Bach

Praeludium

BWV 846

J. S. Bach

Sarabande

HWV 437 / IV

G. F. Händel

Var. I

25
29
Var. II
33
37
41
45

Air con Variazioni

HWV 430 / IV

G. F. Händel

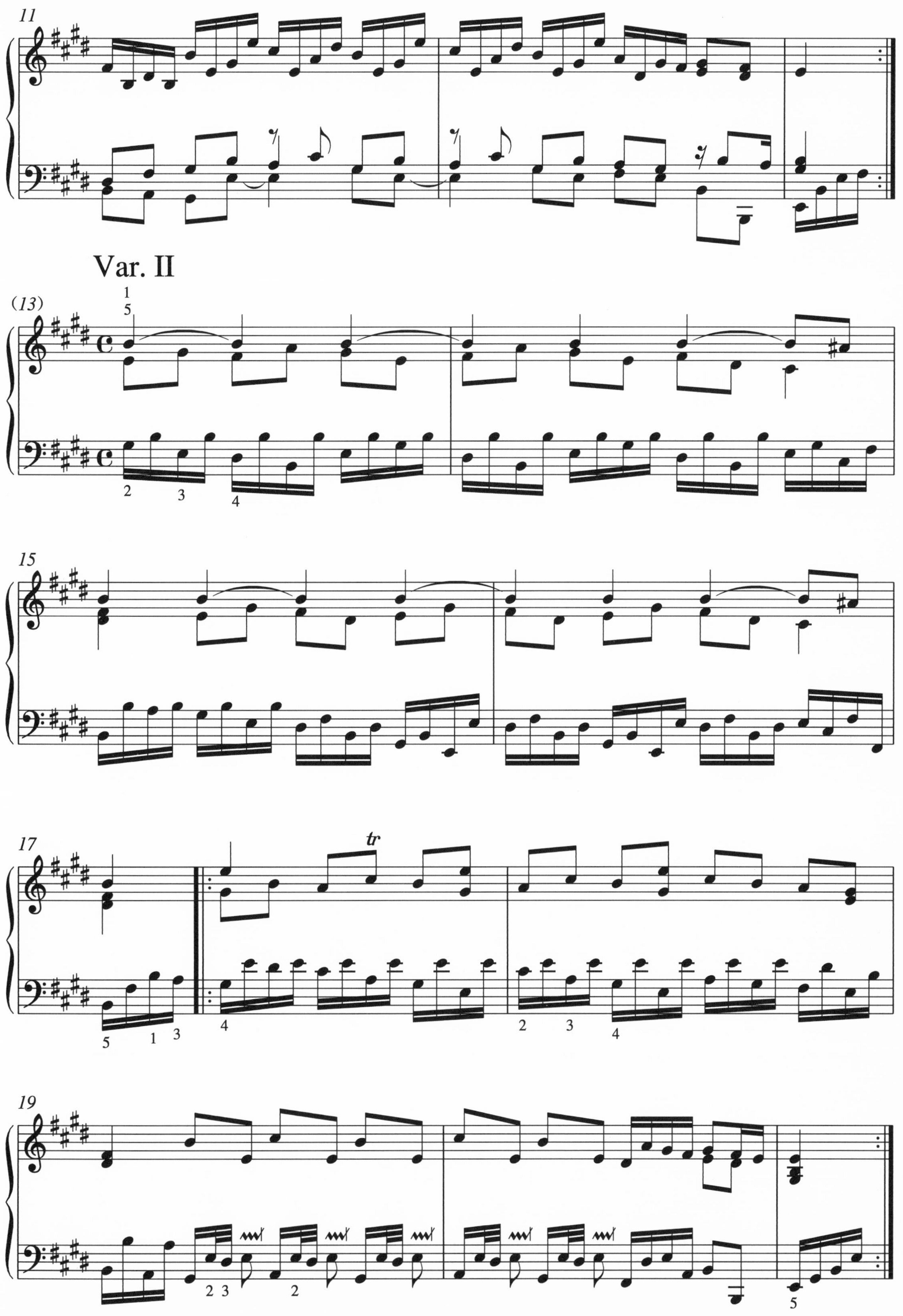

11
Var. II
(13)
15
17
tr
19

Var. III
Var. IV

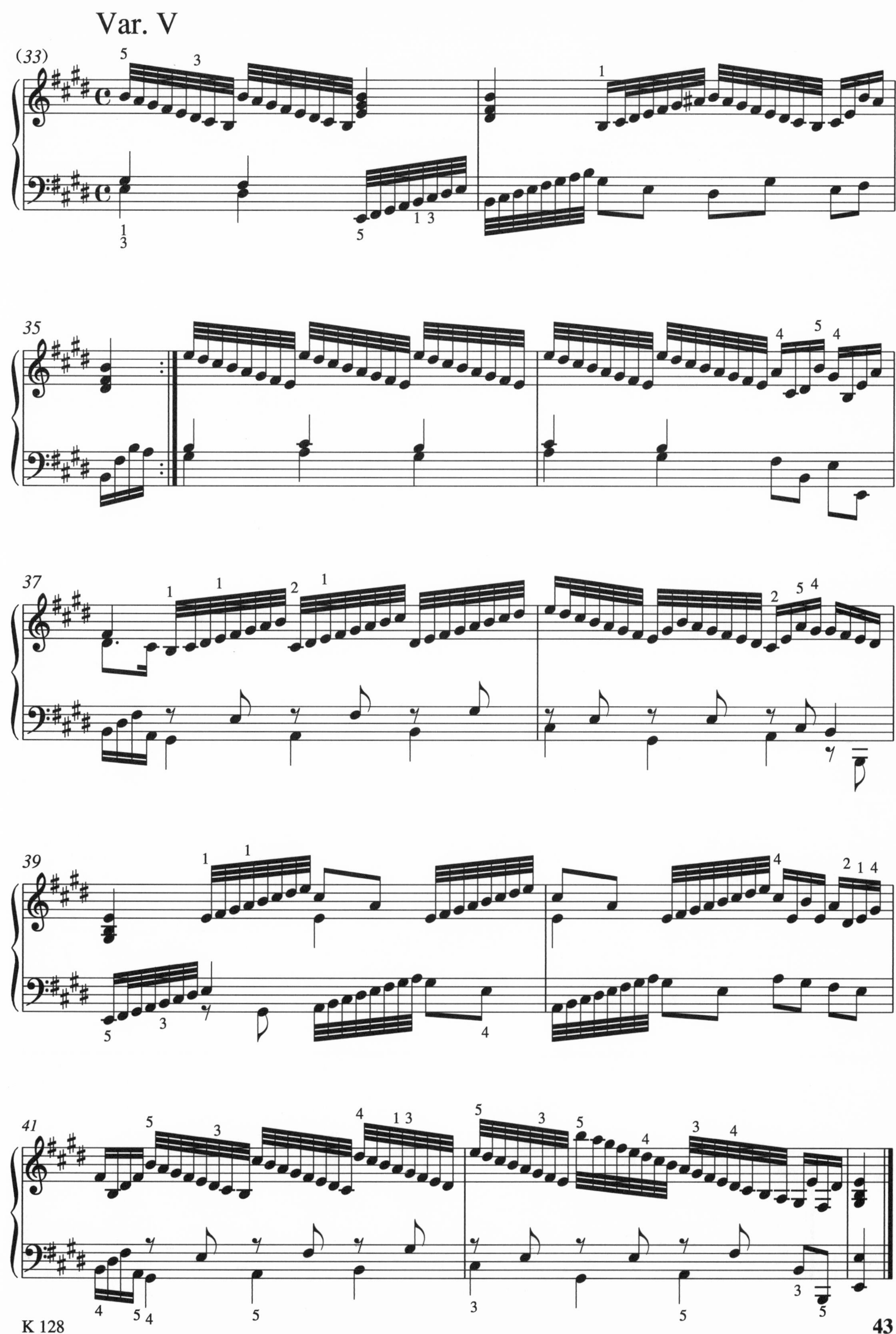
Var. V

Chaconne

Var. III

Var. IV

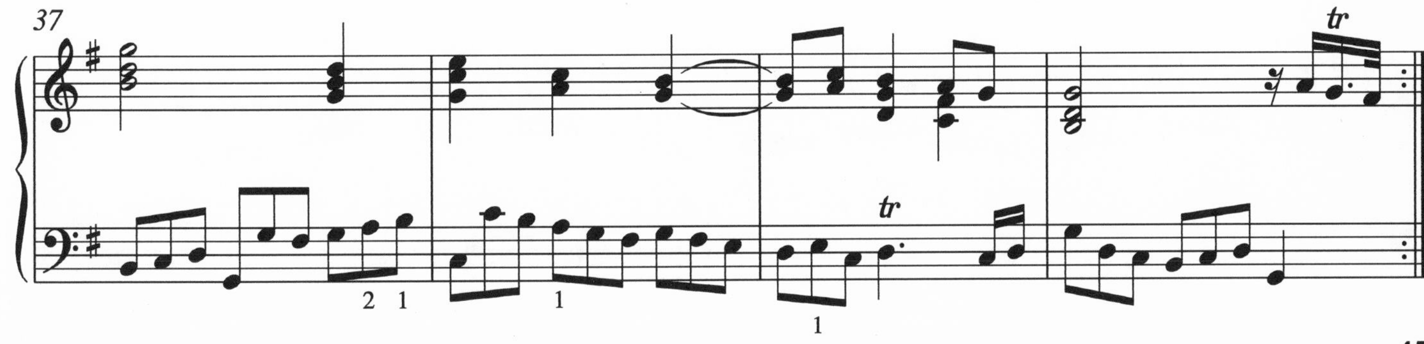

Var. V
Var. VI
Var. VII
tr.

Var. VIII
Var. IX
Adagio

Var. X
Var. XI
Var. XII
tr

Var. XIII
Var. XIV
Var. XV

Var. XVI
Var. XVII
Var. XVIII

Var. XIX
153
157
Var. XX
161
165
Var. XXI
169
173
tr

Sonata

K 1, L 366

D. Scarlatti

Sonata

K 9, L 413

D. Scarlatti

Sonata

K 98, L 325

D. Scarlatti

K 128

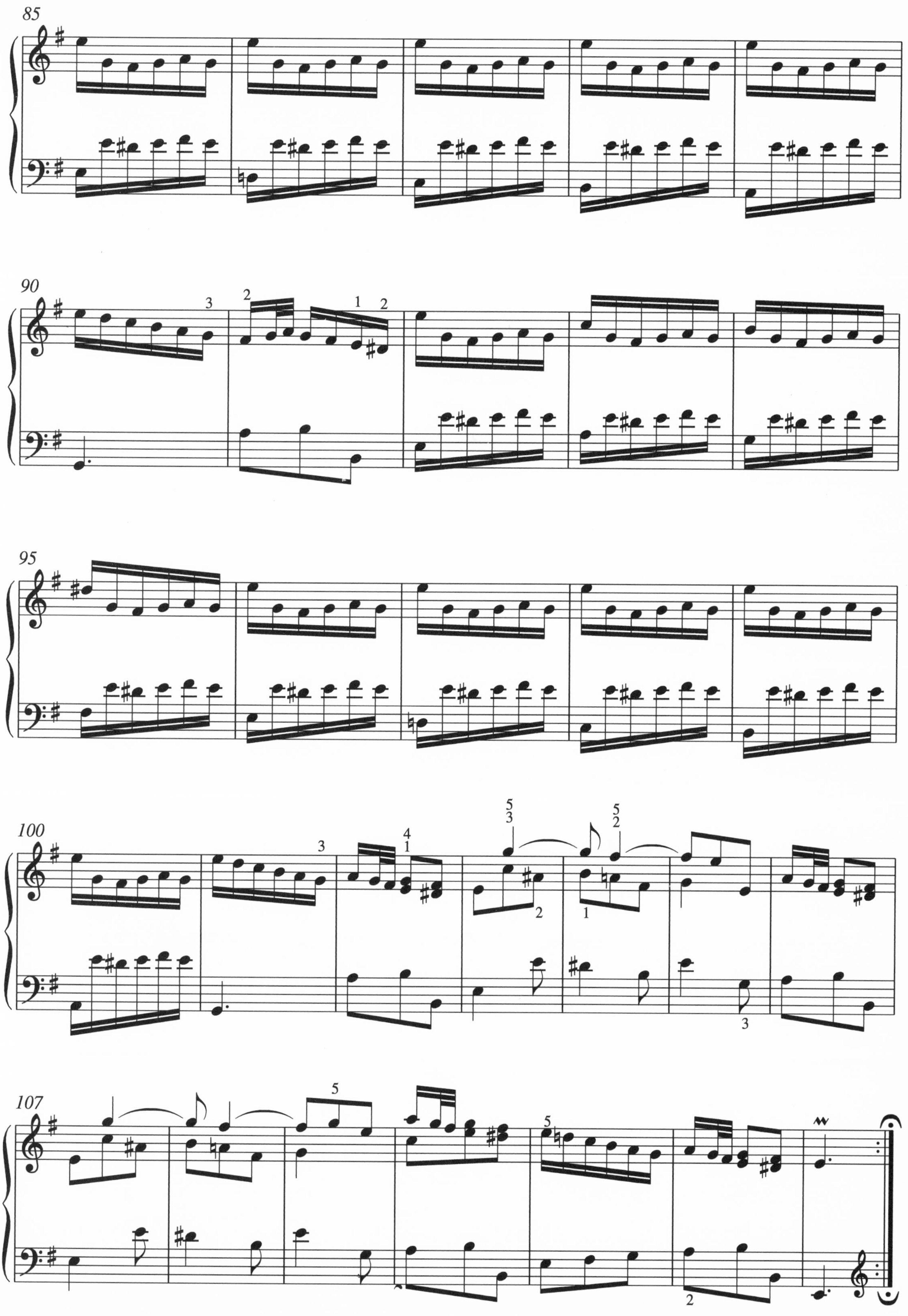
85
90
95
100
107

Sonata

K 96, L 465

K 128

mutandi i deti

164
m.s.
171
m.s.
177
185
194
203

Sonata

K 113, L 345

D. Scarlatti

m.s.
m.s.

m.s.

m.s.

Solfeggio

C. Ph. E. Bach

16
p
f
19
22
p
f
26
p
f
p
f
29
p
f
32

Variationen

über das Lied "Ich schlief, da träumte mir"

C. Ph. E. Bach

Var. II

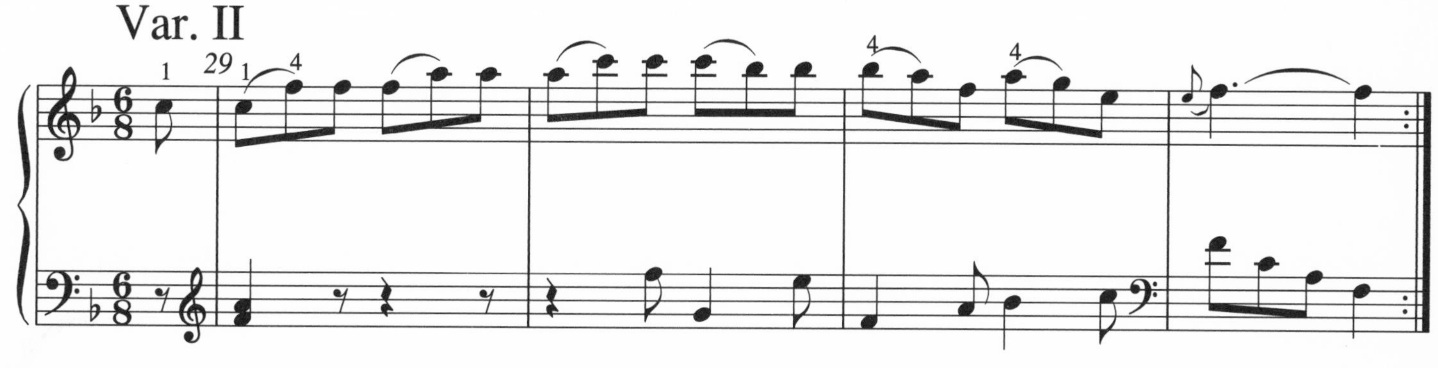

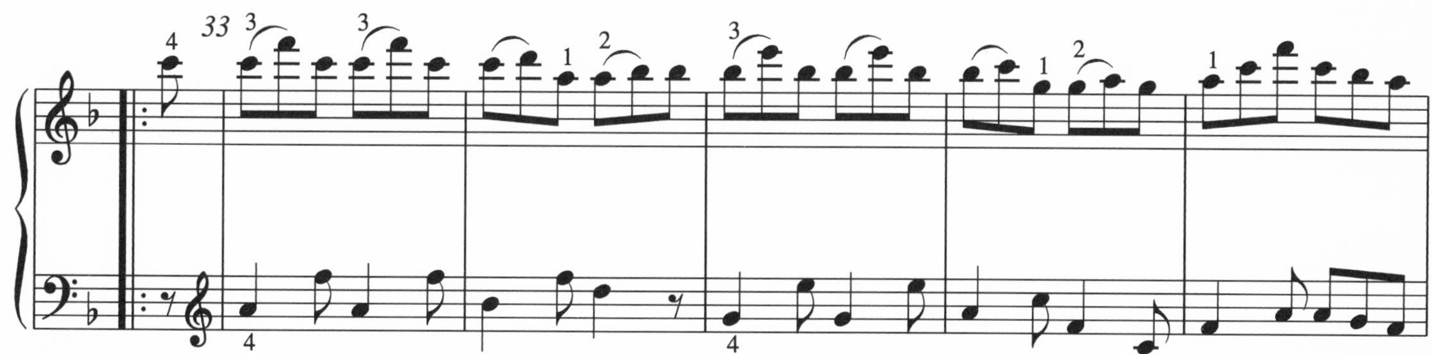

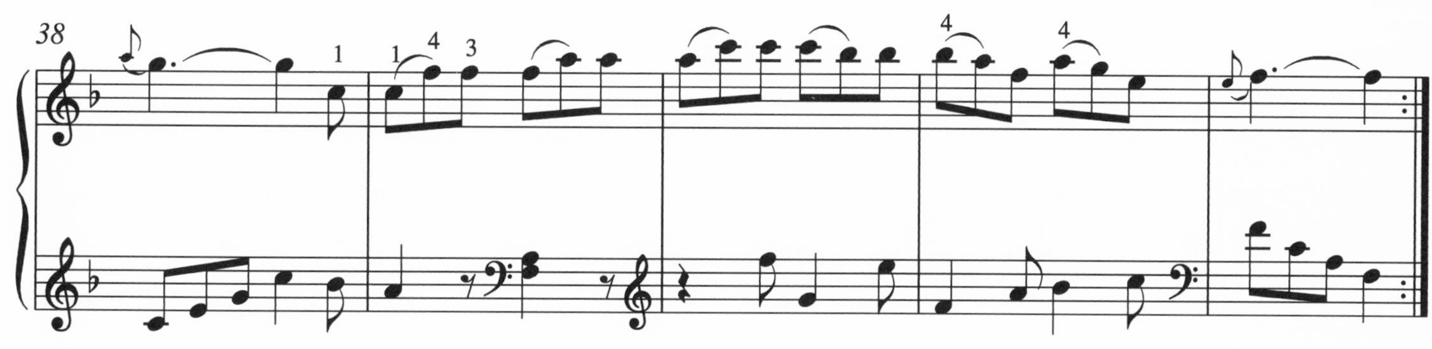

Var. III

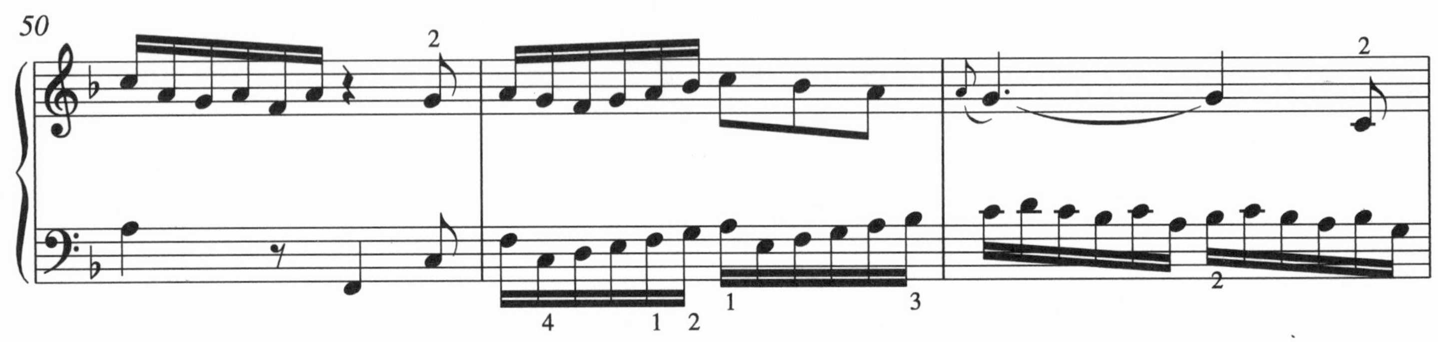

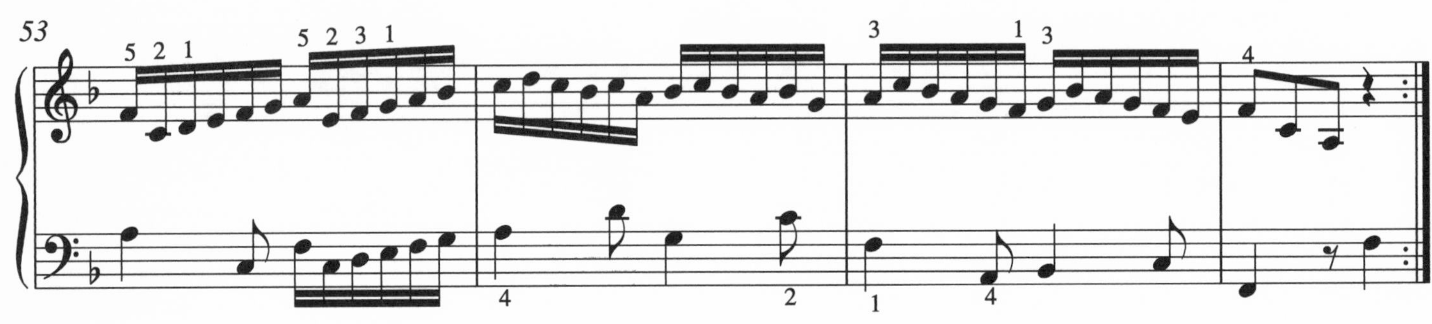

Var. IV

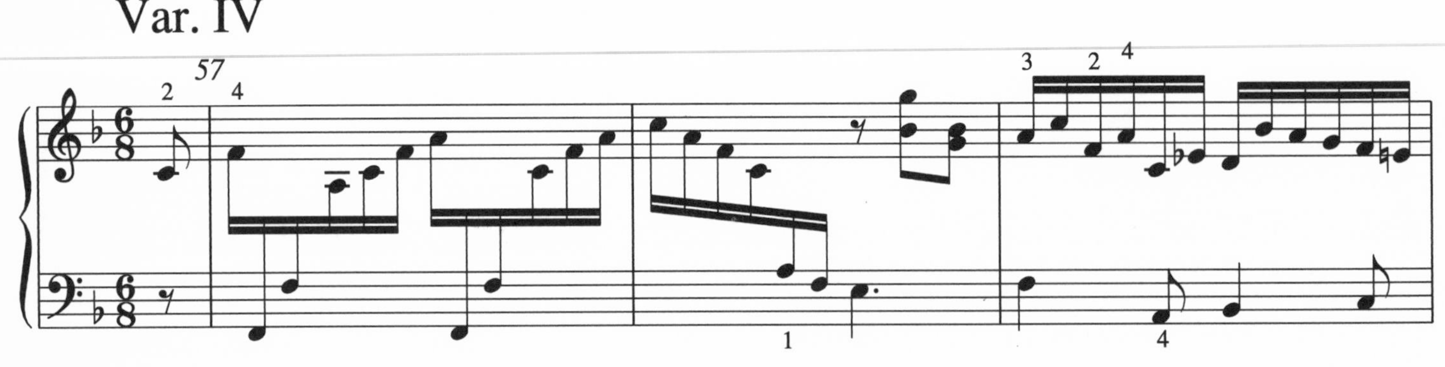

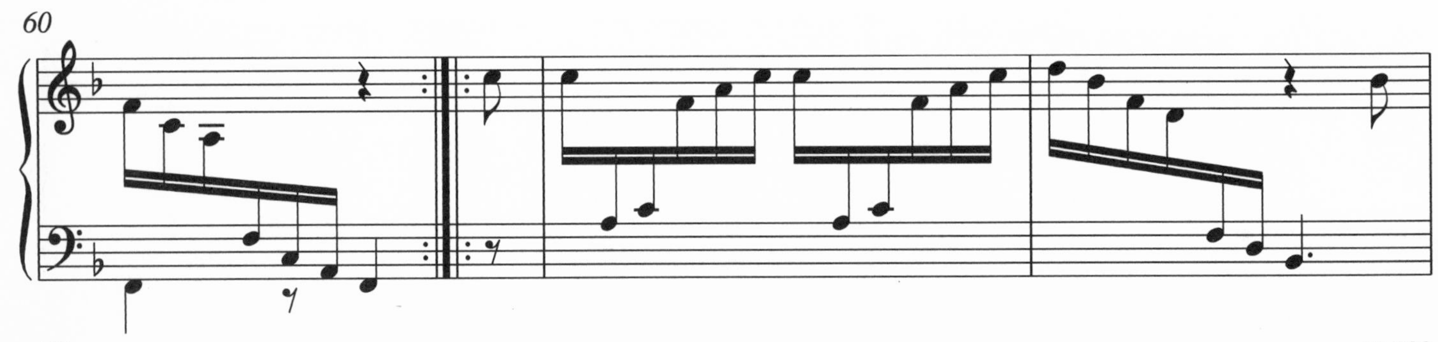

Var. V

Var. VI

Tempo di menuetto

Ochsen - Menuett

Trio
Menuetto da Capo

La Roxolane

Air varié

Var. II
p
f
cresc.
dim.
Var. III
p dolce
mf
cresc.

Var. IV
p
legato
cresc.
f
decresc.
p
p
mf
decresc.
p
sf
p cresc.
rf
p
Var. V
dolce

cresc.

Rondo alla Turca

KV 331 (300[i]) / III

W. A. Mozart

33
p
38
43
48
53
f
59

65
p
70
76
82
tr
f
p
89
f
93
Coda
1.
2.

97
102
107
p
p
112
f
117
122

Fantasie

KV 397 (385g)

W. A. Mozart

cresc.
cresc.
cresc.

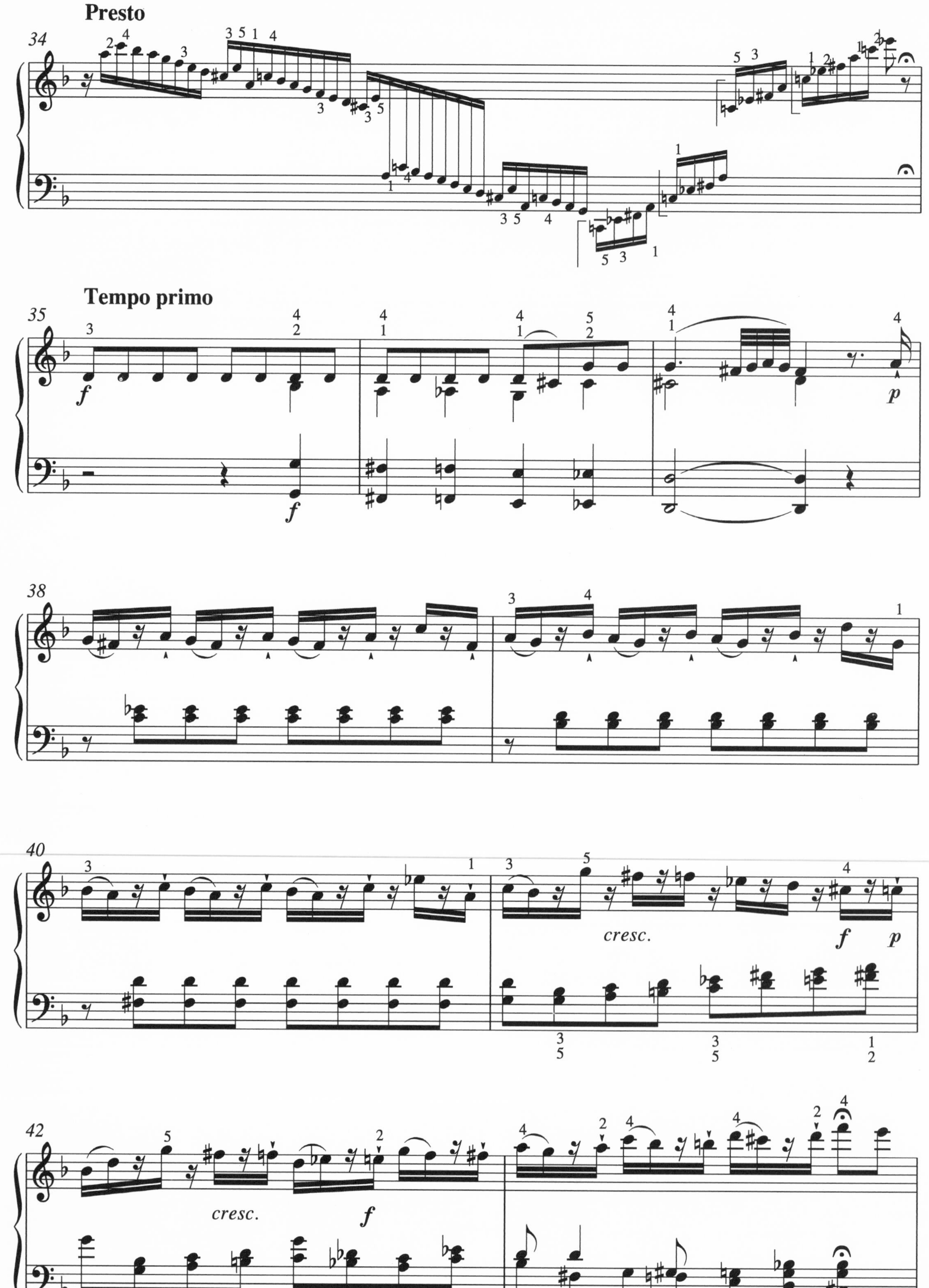
Presto
34
Tempo primo
35
38
40
cresc.
42
cresc.

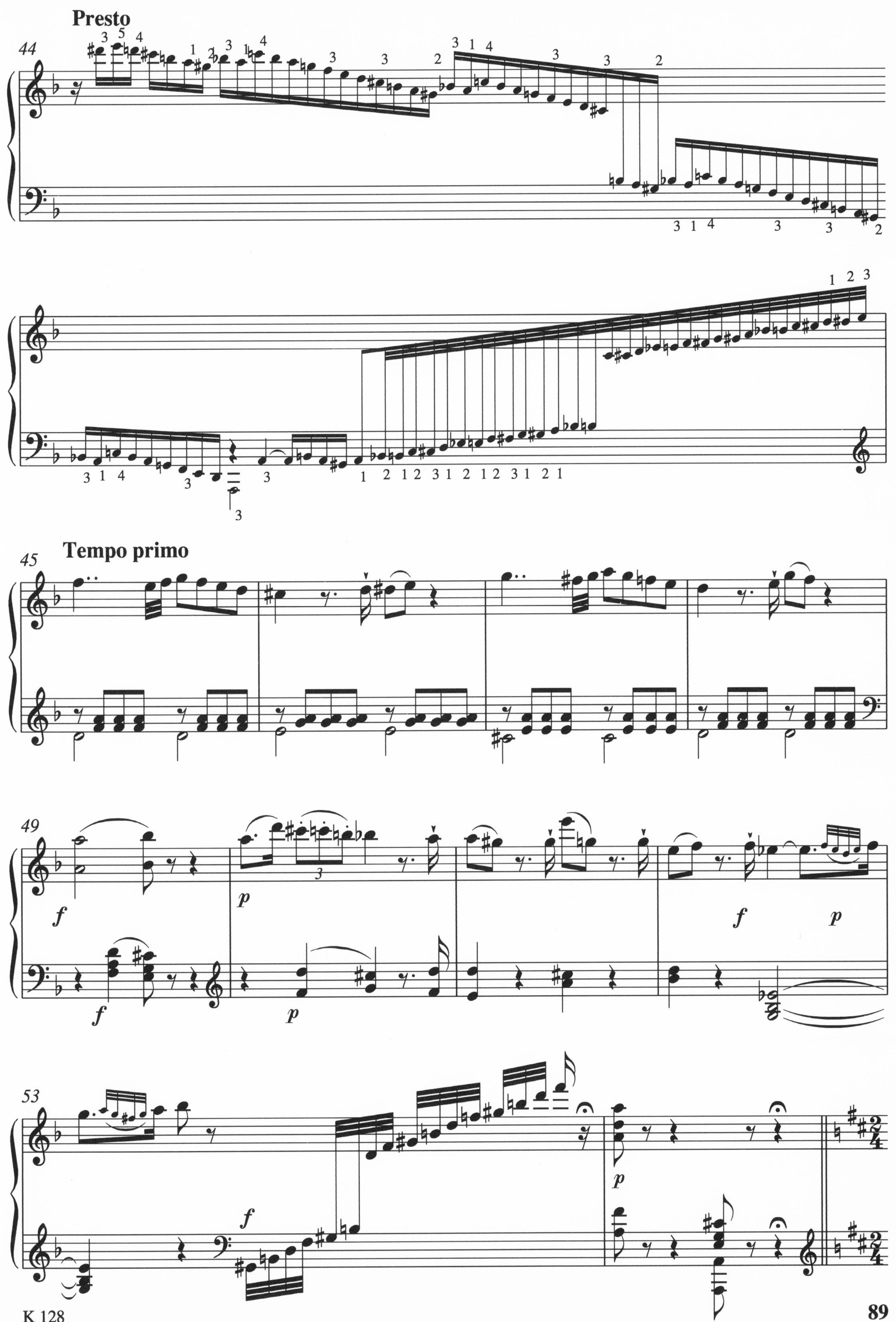

Presto
Tempo primo

Allegretto
dolce
1.
2.

rallentando

Rondo

KV 485

W. A. Mozart

21
25
29
33
37

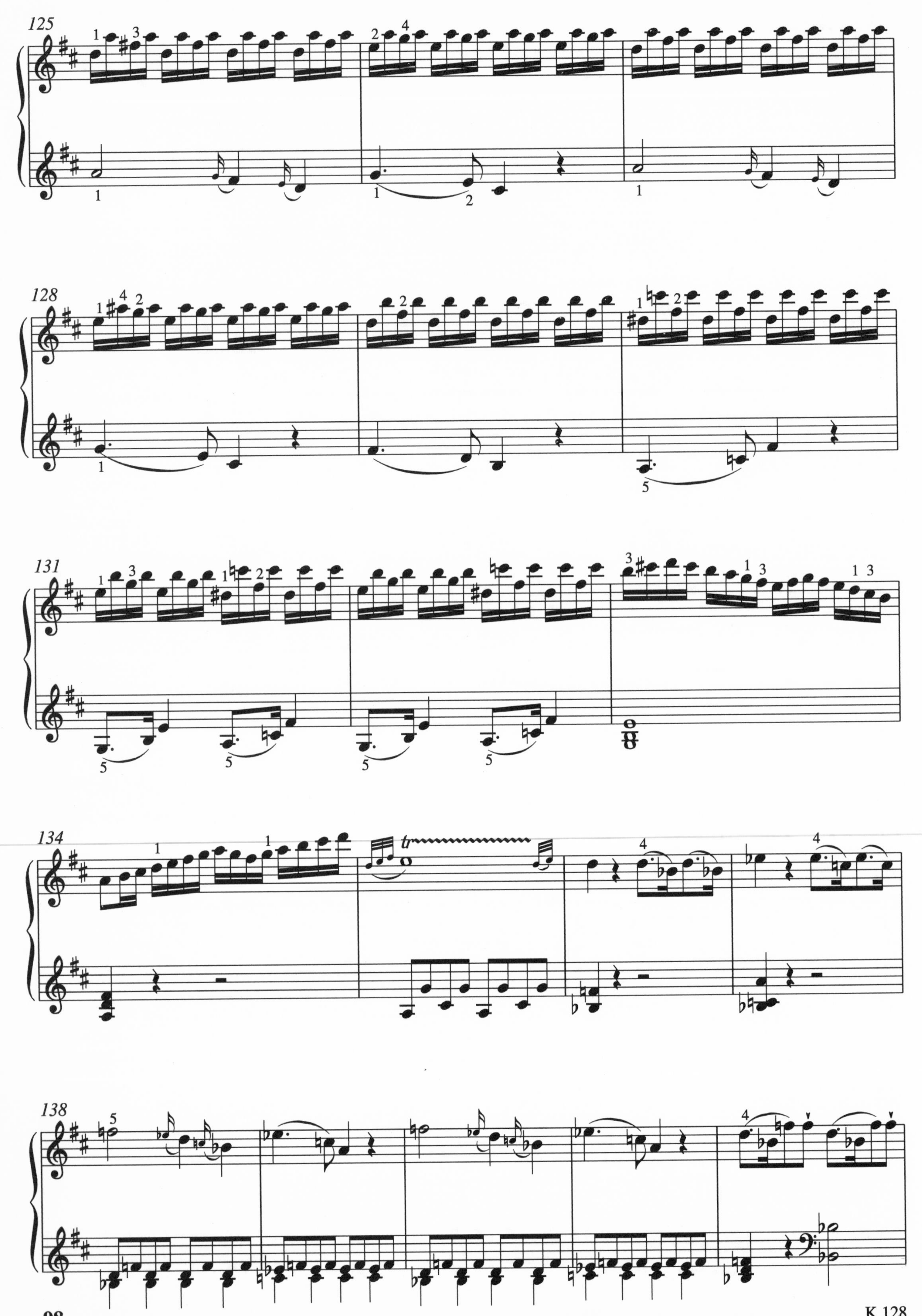
125
128
131
134
138

cresc.
p
calando
pp

6 Ecossaisen

WoO 83

L. van Beethoven

49
f
57
3.
65
73
81
f
89

4.

97

105

113

f

121

145
f
153
161
6.
2 4 2
1
3 1
1
169
1
177
f
185

" Für Elise "

WoO 59

27
32
36
41
47
Ped.
*

53
Ped.
*
59
64
69
74
pp

79
8
83
88
93
98
Ped.
*

Bagatell

Op. 33, No.2

Scherzo

L. van Beethoven

cresc.
p
sf
f
Trio

61
67
cresc.
73
79
87

95
103
111
119
cresc.
128
decresc.

Bagatell

Op. 33, No.3

L. van Beethoven

pp
cresc.
p
sf
sf
pp
cresc.
p
sf
sf
sf
cresc.
f
sf
sf
p
sf
sf
cresc.
f
sf
sf
p
p
cresc.
f
ff

Bagatell

Op. 119, No. 1

L. van Beethoven

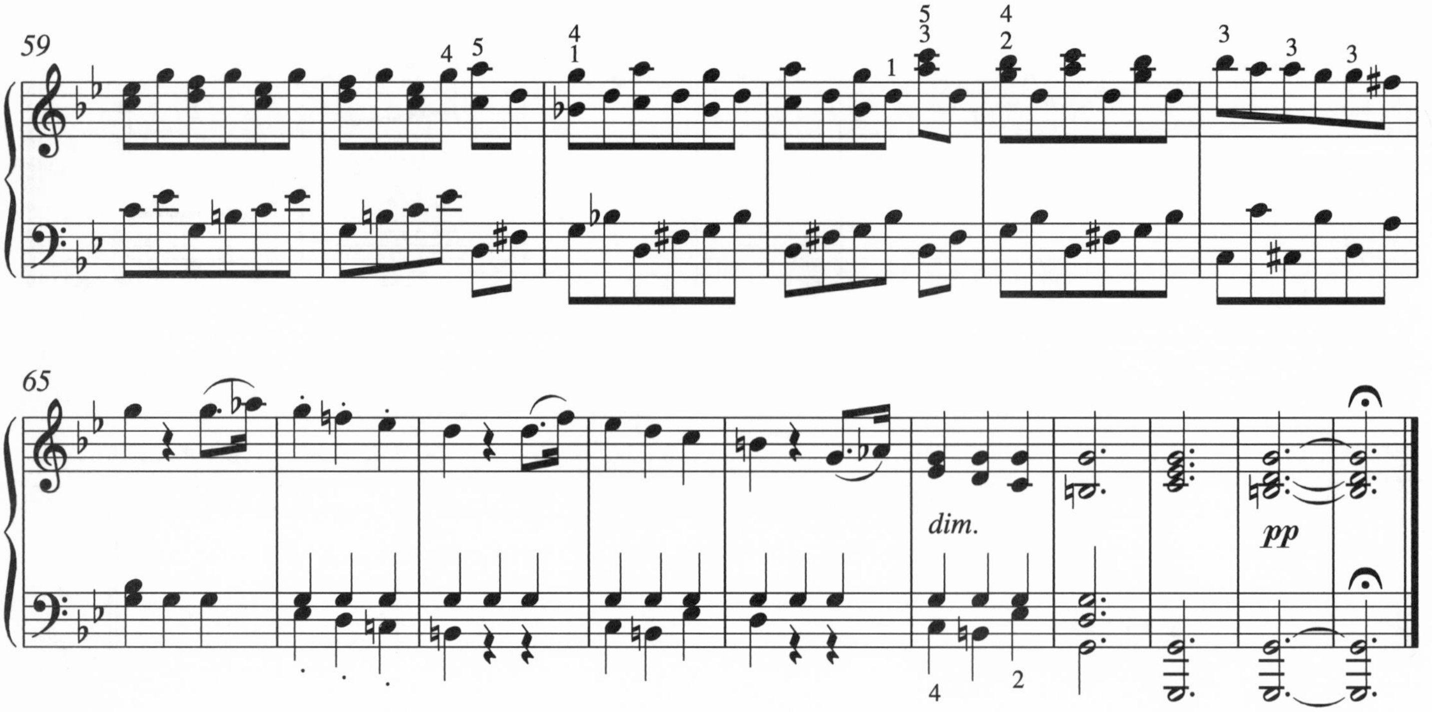

Bagatell

Op.119,No. 9

L.van Beethoven

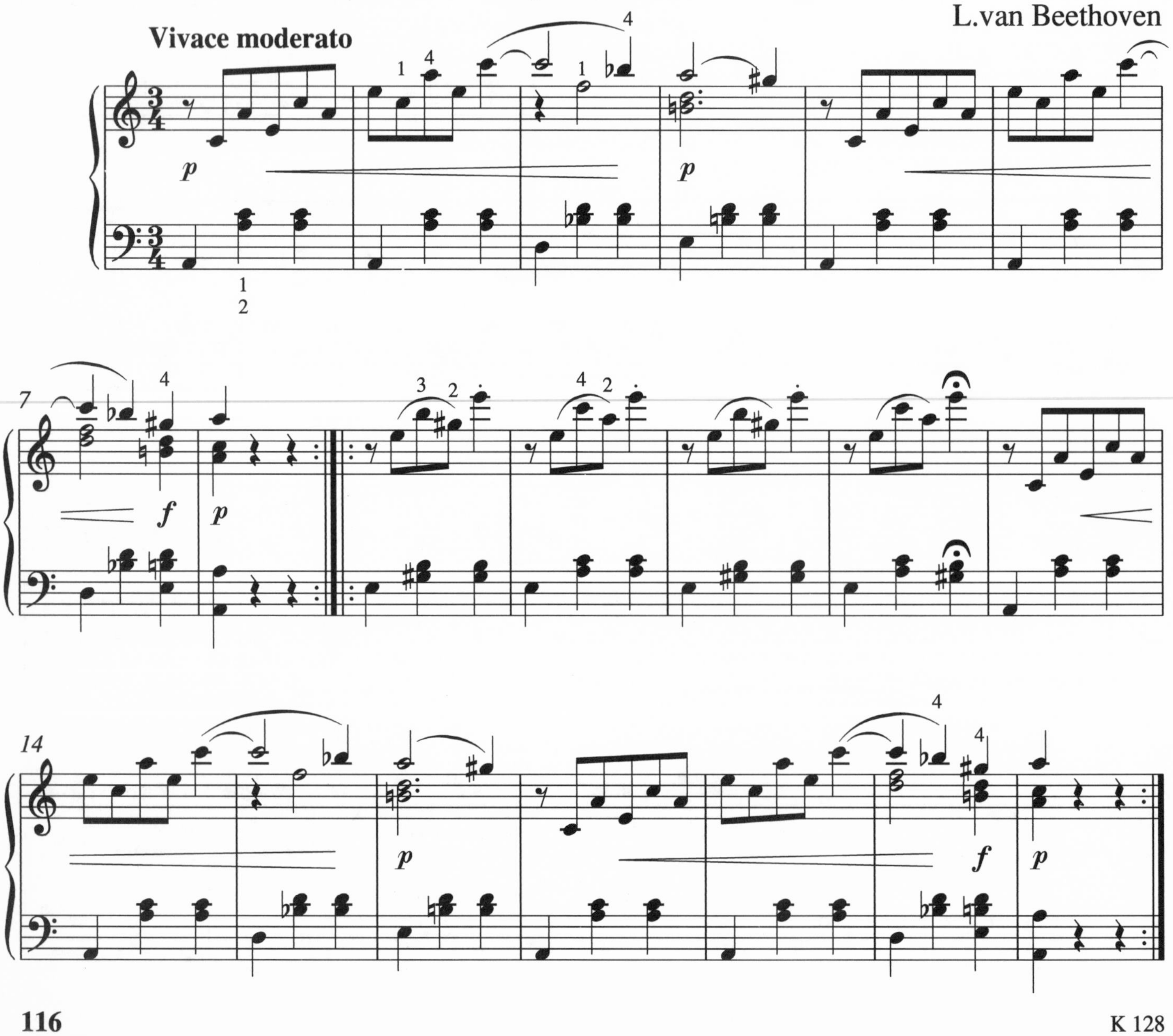

Vivace moderato

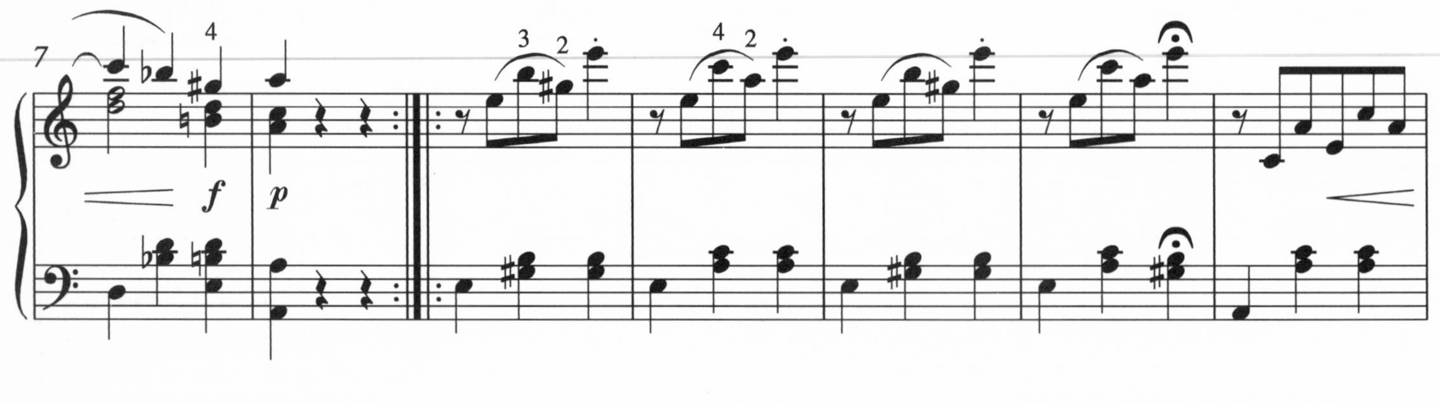

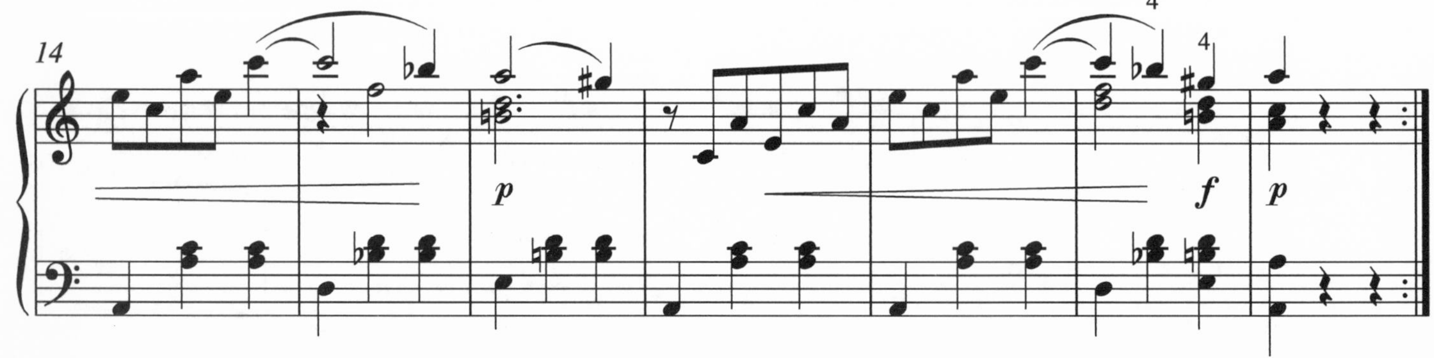

Rondo

Op. 51, No.1

sf
sf
sf
cresc.
f
p
cresc.

33
decresc.
p
37
cresc.
sf p
41
sf
decresc.
pp
45
49
tr
f

52
54
56
58
60
sf
ff
p

cresc.
f
sf
sf
sf
sf
calando

74
77
80
sf
83
85
87

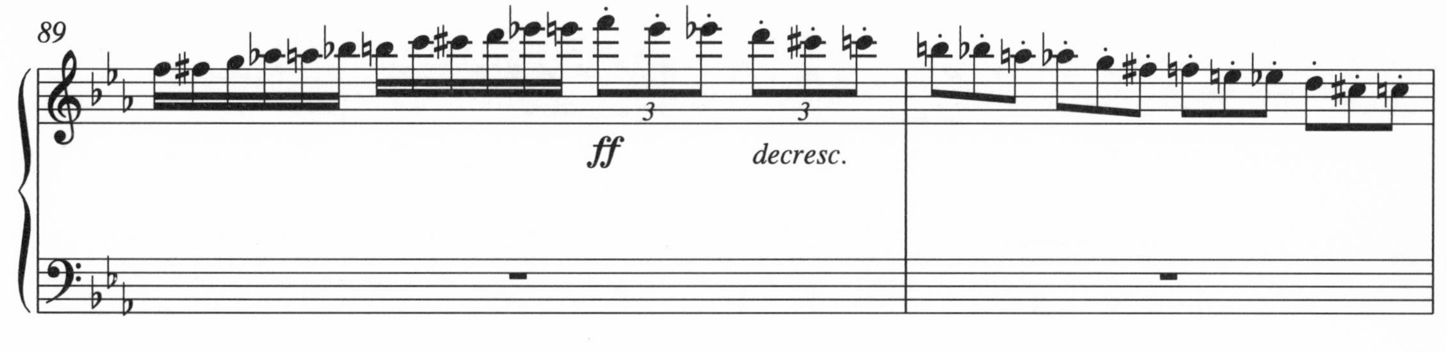
89
ff
decresc.

91
p

94

97
sf

101

104
ritard.
pp
108
legato
111
cresc.
114
f
sfp
117
f
fp

120
p
123
sf
sf
126
sf
sf
128
p
sfp
132
rinf.
rinf.
cresc.
ff

Momento Capriccioso

Op. 12

23
28
dolce

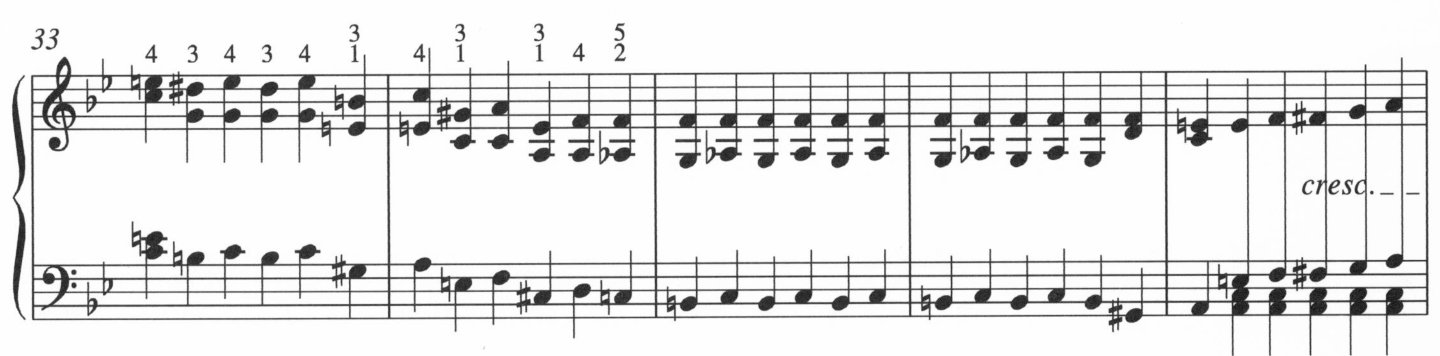
33
cresc.

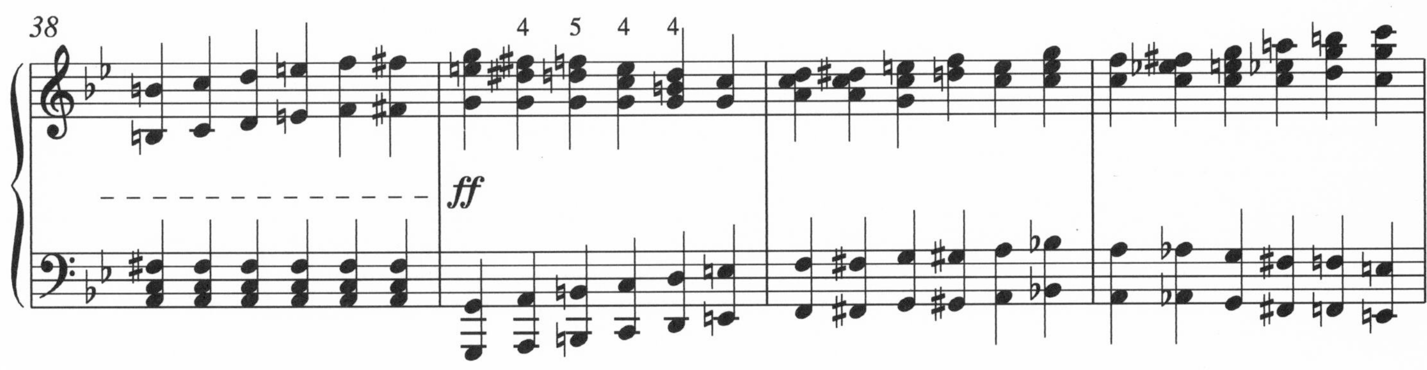
38
ff

42
più cresc.
pp

47
ff
52
55
58
61
rinforzando
64
ff

rinforzando
sf pp dolce
ppp
pp
poco a poco cresc.
ff

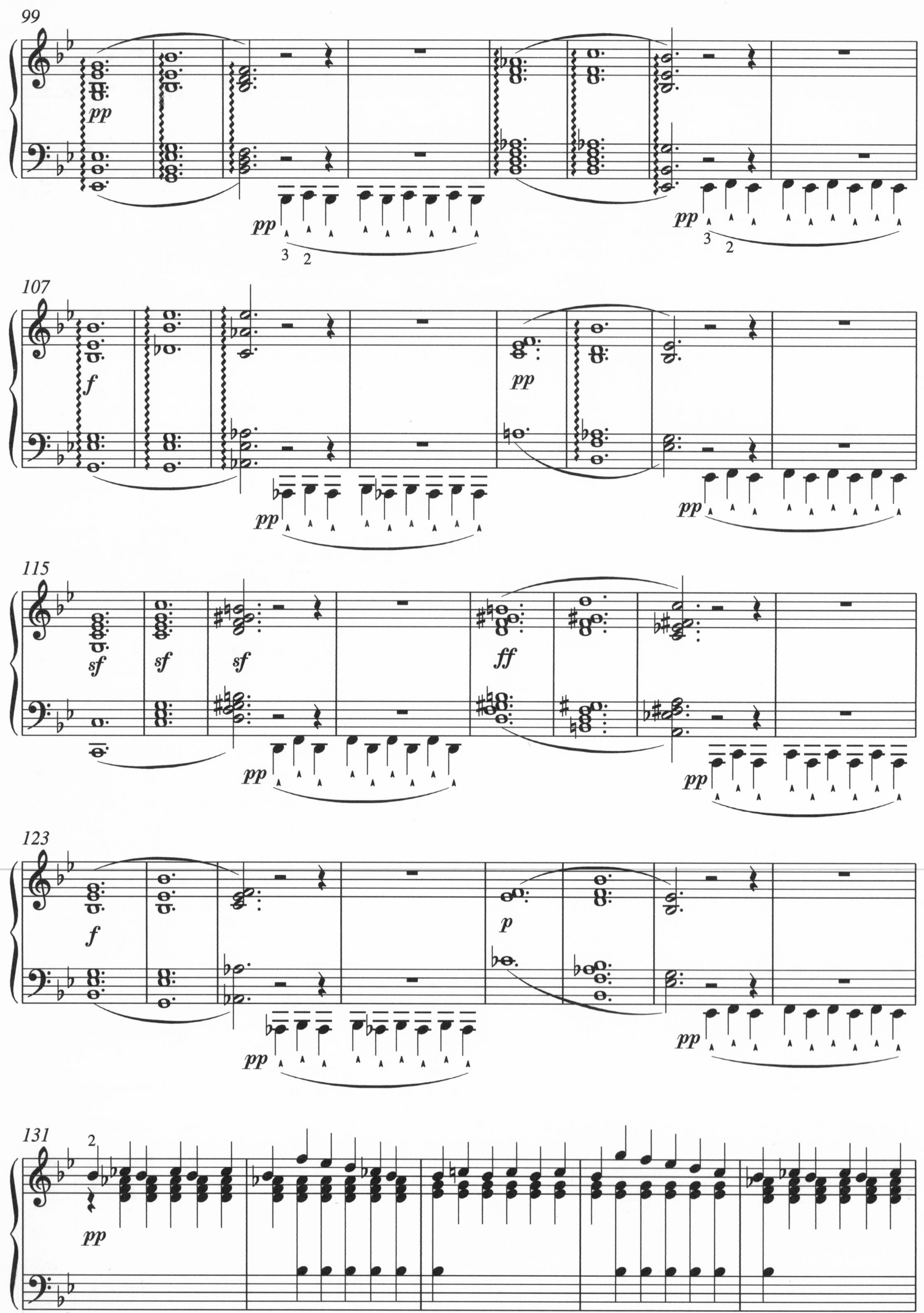
99
pp
pp
3
2
pp
3
2
107
f
pp
pp
pp
115
sf
sf
sf
ff
pp
pp
123
f
p
pp
pp
131
2
pp

136
5
1
4
3
2
1
1
4

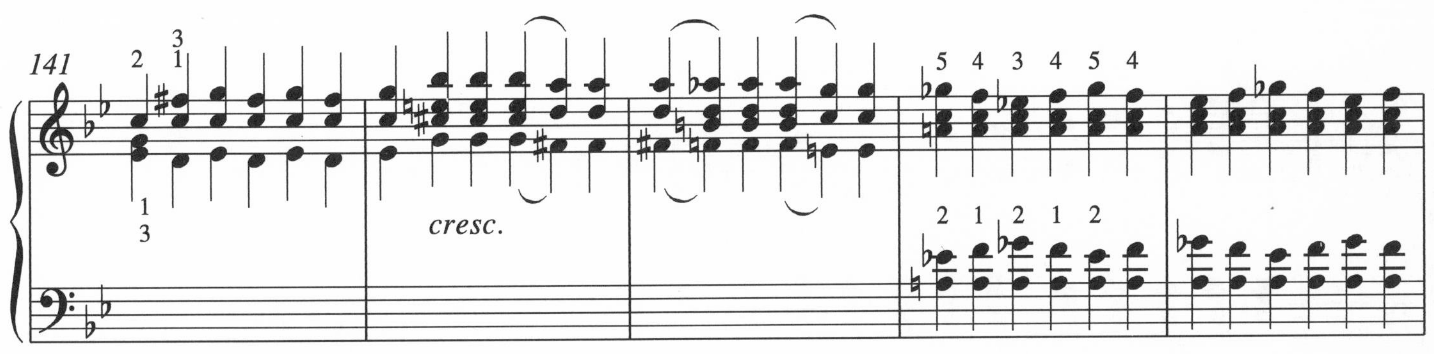
141
2
3
1
1
3
cresc.
5
4
3
4
5
4
2
1
2
1
2

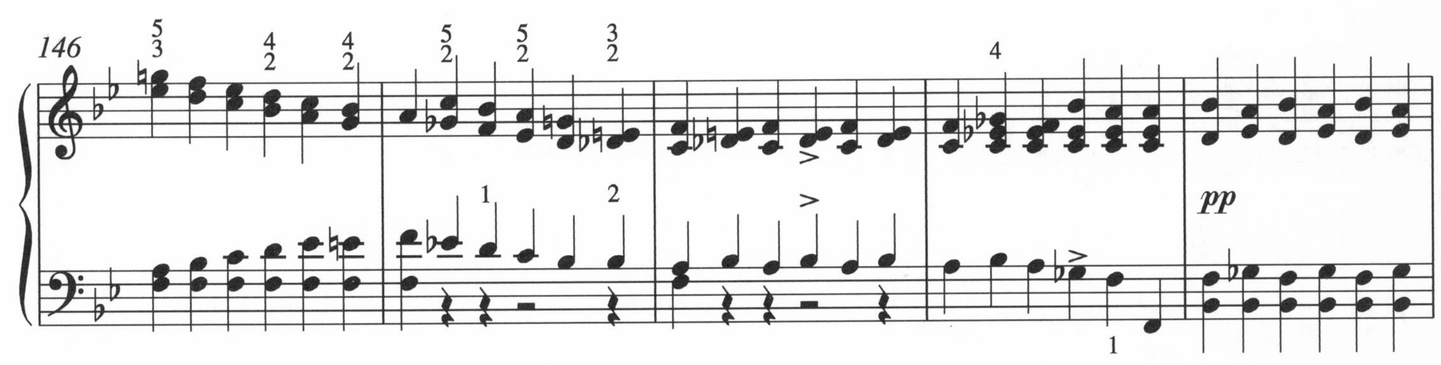
146
5
3
4
2
4
2
5
2
5
2
3
2
1
2
4
1
pp

151
2

156
cresc.
f
ff

161
165
169
poco rall. a tempo
pp
174
179
perdendo
pp
ff

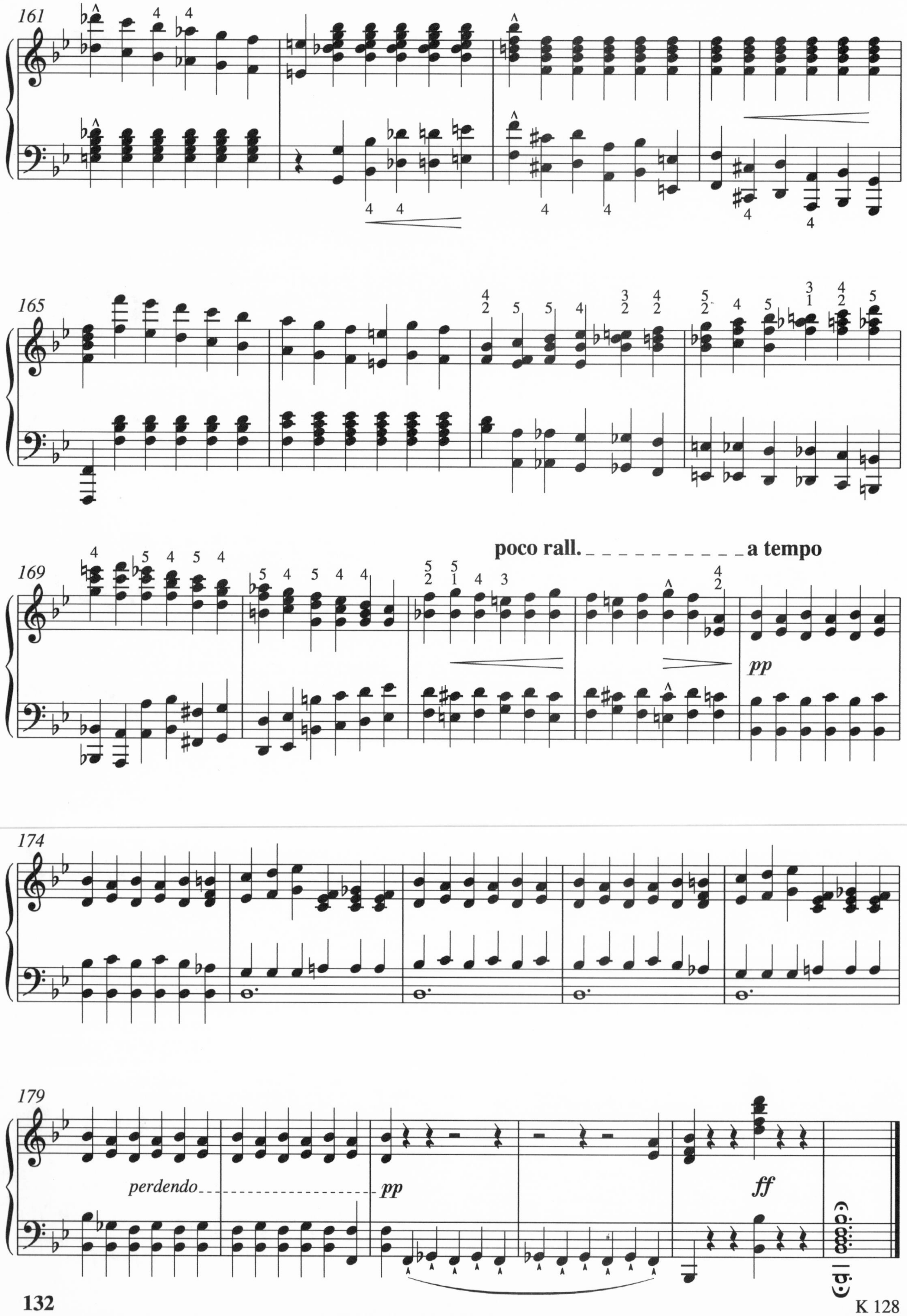

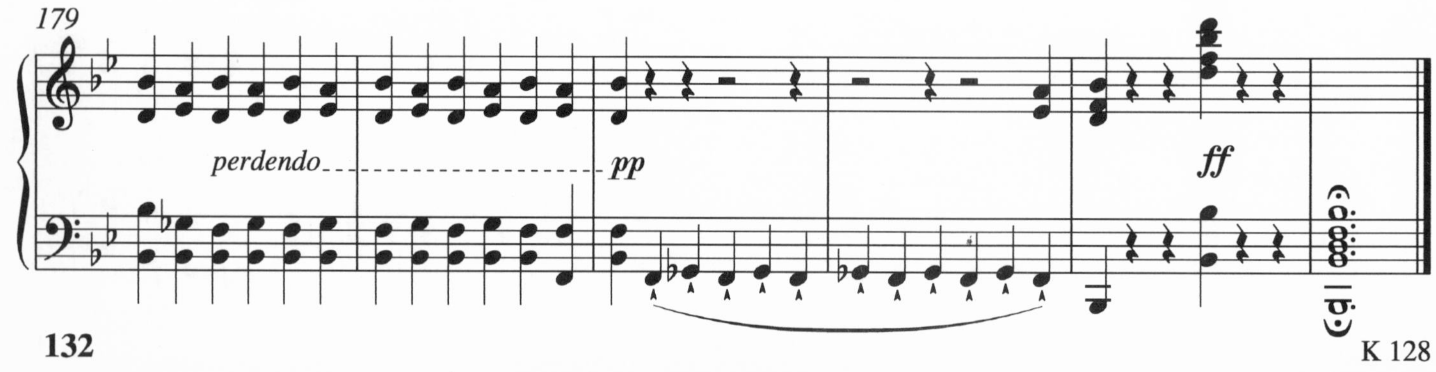

Aufforderung zum Tanz

(Rondeau brillante)

Op. 65

Invitation to the Dance L'invitation à la valse

C. M. von Weber

Allegro vivace
ff
molto dolce
brillante ma grazioso
sempre legato
cresc.
f
ff sempre legato

fp
p sempre legato
ff
wiegend
p

pp
sempre legato
legato e cresc.
wiegend
p

cresc.
ff passionato
decresc.
p
Vivace
ff
ff

ff
p
sempre legato
cresc.
f
ff
ritard. un poco
decresc.

a tempo
pp lusingando
ff
ff sempre
decresc.
p
ff

303
ff
Ped.
311
molto dolce
scherzando
319
brillante
327
sempre legato
333
cresc.
f
339
sempre legato

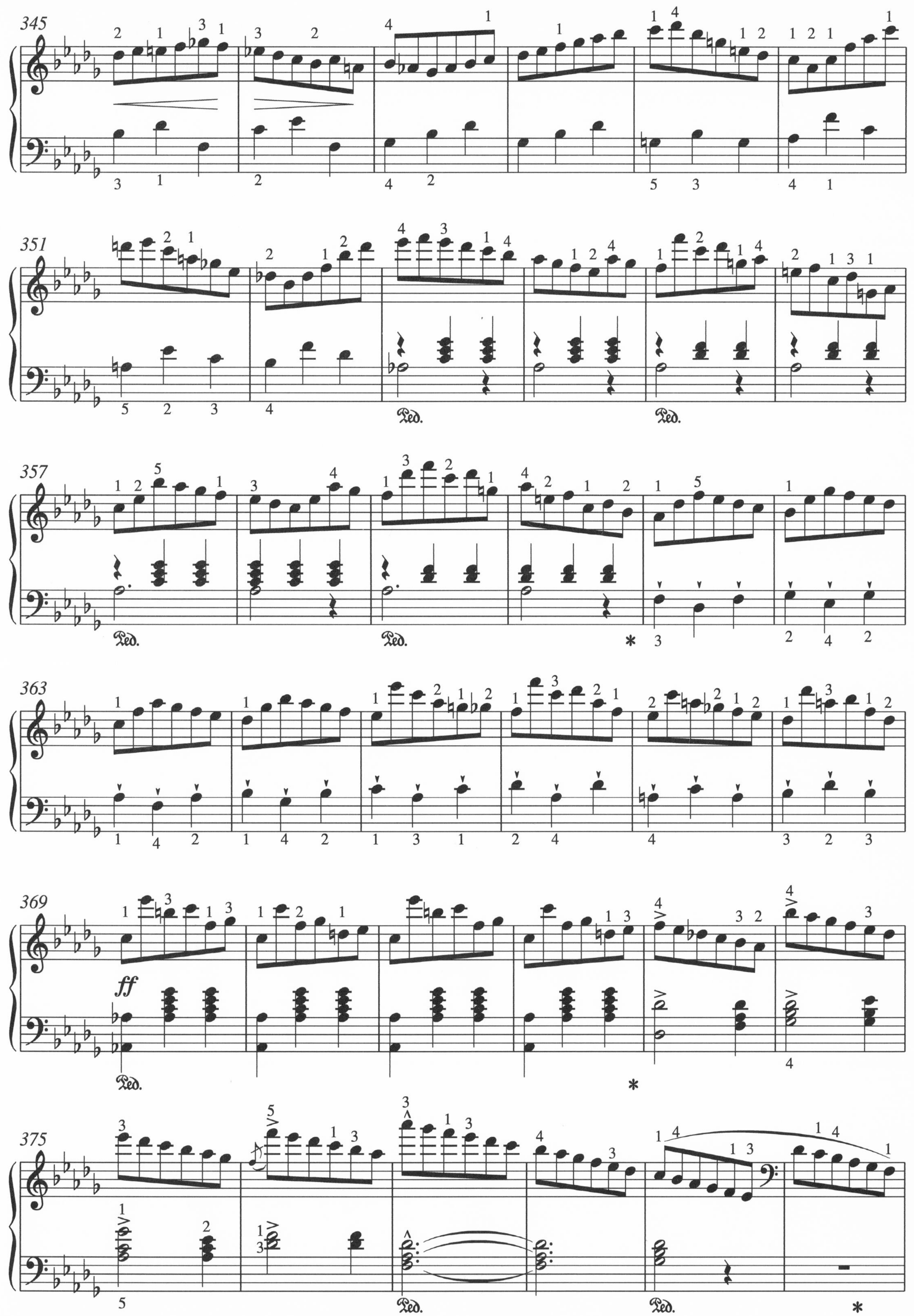
345
351
357
363
369
375
ff
Ped.

381
387
394
400
406
Moderato
413
dim.

Scherzo

D 593

F. Schubert

Trio
legato

pp
p
Scherzo da Capo

Allegretto

D 915

F. Schubert

31
f
ff
decresc.
37
p
pp
cresc.
f
43
ff
ffz
ffz
p
50
pp
f
55
ff
decresc.
p
pp

61
pp
fp
67
pp
73
cresc.
3
4
2
pp
80
f
pp
pp
p
87
decresc.
pp

93
p
decresc.
pp
99
p
cresc.
106
f
ff
fz
ffz
113
p
pp
f
119
ff
decresc.
p
pp

Moment musical

Op. 94, Nr. 3, D 780

F. Schubert

pp
ppp
dim.
dim.

Impromptu

Op. post. 142 , D 935

F. Schubert

K128

Trio
p
decresc.
pp

59
f
63
cresc.
67
ff
fz
71
75
p
decresc.
79

83
87
decresc.
pp
91
decresc.
4
5
95
sempre legato
pp
100
107

115
121
128
135
142
rit.
cresc.

© 1995 for this edition by Könemann Music Budapest Kft.
H–1093 Budapest, Közraktár utca 10.

K 128/3

Distributed worldwide by
Könemann Verlagsgesellschaft mbH, Bonner Str. 126.
D-50968 Köln

Responsible co-editor: István Máriássy
Production: Detlev Schaper
Cover design: Peter Feierabend
Technical editor: Dezső Varga

Printed by Kossuth Printing House Co., Budapest
Printed in Hungary

ISBN 963 8303 41 7